SALESFORCE APEX QUESTION BANK

2022

TechPro Education LLC.

Salesforce Apex Question Bank

CopyRight c TechPro Education LLC, 2022

All publication rights of this work belong to TechPro Education LLC.

ISBN: 979-8-9862229-1-2

www.techproeducation.com
Published: April 2022

PREFACE

What is Apex?

Apex is a strongly typed, object-oriented programming language that allows developers to execute flow and transaction control statements on Salesforce servers in conjunction with calls to the API.

Using syntax that looks like Java and acts like database stored procedures, Apex enables developers to add business logic to most system events, including button clicks, related record updates, and Visualforce pages.

Apex Code can be initiated by Web service requests and from triggers on objects.

Apex provides built-in support for unit test creation and execution. It includes test results that indicate how much the code coverage is, and which parts of your code could be more efficient.

Salesforce ensures that all custom Apex code works as expected by executing all unit tests before any platform upgrades.

Why should I learn Apex?

i) In the IT sector, you should learn at least one programming language, regardless of the field of study, because it is not possible to understand the logic of IT without learning a programming language.

ii) The mechanism working behind the Salesforce admin part is understood.

iii) Becoming a salesforce admin is easier than becoming a salesforce developer. For this reason, many people target to become a Salesforce Admin at first. Learning Apex coding language puts you a few steps ahead of your competitors, enabling you to find a job faster with higher salaries.

iv) People who can do several jobs in the IT sector are critical for companies. You can become an indispensable element by learning both the admin and the development parts.

v) Contrary to popular belief, it is easy to become a Salesforce developer with the right content and methods. Even though becoming a salesforce admin part is easier than becoming a salesforce developer, it would be wise to spend a few more weeks becoming a salesforce developer because of the unbelievable job opportunities.

About the book

Apex Question Bank consists of two parts.

In the first part, you will learn how to read Apex code, how the Apex methods are used, and how other important concepts are used with 129 multiple choice test questions separated by subject.

In the second part, you will write code to perform tasks that are compatible with real life. In this part, you will see 120 free response questions with more than one solution to a problem to give you different perspectives. You will have the opportunity to compare these solutions with your own solutions.

In the upcoming days, we will publish video recordings that contain the solutions to every problem in this book.

TechPro Education wishes you healthy and successful days.

ABOUT THE AUTHOR

Mr. Alptekin has more than 10 years of teaching experience and touched many people's lives by teaching development courses.

Mr. Alptekin is a very passionate instructor. He is currently teaching development classes such as APEX, SOQL, JAVA at TechPro Educations for future developers.

Mr. Alptekin holds Bachelor's in Mathematics and an Associate degree in Computer Science. He has Oracle JAVA, AWS, and Scrum Mater certified. He is also a high-rated Udemy instructor. Mr. Alptekin is one of the TechPro Education co-founders as well.

CONTENTS

PART 1 - TESTS

PART 2 - APEX QUESTIONS

TESTS

VARIABLES

1. .... means taking the programmer-readable text in your program file and converting it to binary codes.
   Which one is true for the blank?
   a) Compile
   b) Variable
   c) Object-Oriented Programming Language
   d) Statement

2. Which <u>ones</u> are true?
   a) A bit is the smallest unit of data in a computer.
   b) A bit has a single binary value, either 0 or 1.
   c) 8 bits are called 1 byte
   d) Data is information processed or stored in a computer.

3. Which one is true to **declare a variable** and **assign a value** to the variable?
   a) Integer x = 12;
   b) Integer x : 12;
   c) 12 = Integer x;
   d) 12 : Integer x;

4. Put the given ones to create a variable and assign a value to the variable
   1) Variable Name
   2) Value
   3) Data Type
   4) Equal Sign
   5) Semicolon
   a) 3 - 1 - 4 - 2 - 5
   b) 3 - 4 - 1 - 2 - 5
   c) 3 - 1 - 2 - 4 - 5
   d) 1 - 3 - 4 - 2 - 5

5. Which <u>ones</u> are true?
   a) Long populationOfTheWorld = 7753000000;
   b) Long populationOfChina = 1500000000;
   c) Decimal price = 14.99;
   d) Boolean isNew = null;

6. What is the output?
   Integer a = 11;
   Integer b = 22;
   System.debug('The sum of a and b is ' + a + b);
   a) The sum of a and b is 1122
   b) The sum of a and b is 33
   c) The code gives an error
   d) 33

7. What is the output?
   Integer a = 5;
   Decimal b = 2.4;
   System.debug('The multiplication of a and b is ' + a*b);
   a) The multiplication of a and b is 12.0
   b) The multiplication of a and b is 12
   c) The multiplication of a and b is 122.4
   d) The code gives an error

8. According to the given image, which ones are true?
   a) **A** displays variables
   b) **B** displays functions
   c) **C** displays class
   d) **D** displays objects

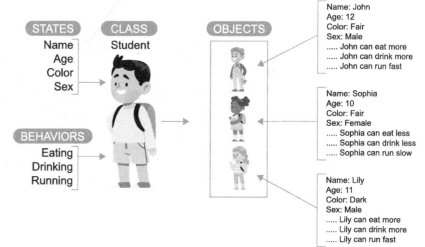

9. Which one is true?
   a) String cityName = 'Miami'
   b) String cityName = "Miami";
   c) String cityName = 'Miami';
   d) String cityName : 'Miami';

10. Coding Standards;
    1) Use **CamelCase** in variable names and method names
    2) If it is possible do not use **repetition**
    3) Make the parenthesis as possible as **simple**
    4) Select appropriate data types to **use the memoryless**
    Which one is <u>not</u> breaking any of the given coding standards?
    a) String nameofstudent = 'Ali Can';
    b) Decimal priceOfShirt = 12.99;
        Decimal priceOfShoes = 23.99;
    c) Decimal priceOfShirt = 12.99, priceOfShoes = 23.99;
        String totalPrice = 'Total price is ' + (5*priceOfShirt + 6*priceOfShoes);
        System.debug(totalPrice);
    d) Long numOfRegisteredStudents = 2300L;

STRING MANIPULATIONS

1. Which one is <u>false</u>?
   a) String **s** = 'apex is easy';
      String **t** = **s**.toUpperCase();
      System.debug(**t**);

      Prints ***APEX is easy*** on the console

   b) String **s** = 'Apex Is Easy';
      String **t** = **s**.toLowerCase();
      System.debug(**t**);

      Prints ***apex is easy*** on the console

   c) String **s** = 'apex is EASY';
      String **t** = **s**.capitalize();
      System.debug(**t**);

      Prints ***Apex is EASY*** on the console

   d) String **s** = 'apex is EASY';
      String **t** = **s**.toLowerCase().capitalize();
      System.debug(**t**);

      Prints ***Apex is easy*** on the console

2. Which code prints "**learn more**" on the console?
   a) String s = 'Teach more learn more';
      String t = s.split(' ')[2] + s.split(' ')[3];
      System.debug(t);
   b) String s = 'Teach more learn more';
      String t = s.split('   ')[2] + '   ' + s.split('   ')[3];
      System.debug(t);
   c) String s = 'Teach more learn more';
      String t = s.split('   ')[3] + '   ' + s.split('   ')[4];
      System.debug(t);
   d) String s = 'Teach more learn more';
      String t = s.split('   ')[3] + s.split('   ')[4];
      System.debug(t);

3. Which codes print "**ALI Can**" on the console?
   a) String **s** = 'ali can';
      String **t** = **s**.split(' ')[0].toUpperCase() + ' ' + **s**.split(' ')[1].capitalize();
      System.debug(**t**);
   b) String **s** = 'ALI CAN';
      String **t** = **s**.split(' ')[0] + ' ' + **s**.split(' ')[1].toLowerCase().capitalize();
      System.debug(**t**);
   c) String **s** = 'ali CAN';
      String **t** = **s**.split(' ')[0].toUpperCase() + ' ' + **s**.split(' ')[1].capitalize();
      System.debug(**t**);
   d) String **s** = 'ALI can';
      String **t** = **s**.split(' ')[0] + ' ' + **s**.split(' ')[1].capitalize();
      System.debug(**t**);

4. Which code converts '   **ali can**   ' to '**Ali**'
   a) String **s** = '   **ali can**   ';
      String **t** = **s**.trim().split(' ')[0].capitalize();
      System.debug(**t**);
   b) String **s** = '   **ali can**   ';
      String **t** = **s**.split(' ')[0].capitalize();
      System.debug(**t**);
   c) String **s** = '   **ali can**   ';
      String **t** = **s**.trim().split(' ')[0].toUpperCase();
      System.debug(**t**);
   d) String **s** = '   **ali can**   ';
      String **t** = **s**.split(' ')[0].toUpperCase();
      System.debug(**t**);

5. Which one is false?
   a) String **s** = '**Ali Can**';
      String **t** = **s**.length();
      System.debug(**t**);
      Prints **7** on the console
   b) String **s** = '**Apex is easy**';
      Integer **t** = **s**.length();
      System.debug(**t**);
      Prints **12** on the console
   c) String **s** = '**Apex is easy**';
      Integer **t** = **s**.split('**e**')[0].length();
      System.debug(**t**);
      Prints **2** on the console
   d) String **s** = '**Apex is easy**';
      Integer **t** = **s**.split('**s**')[2].length();
      System.debug(**t**);
      Prints **1** on the console

6. String s = 'Apex is Apex';
   Which ones are true?
   a) System.debug(s.indexOf('**e**'));
      Prints **3** on the console
   b) System.debug(s.indexOf('**Apex**'));
      Prints **0** on the console
   c) System.debug(s.indexOf('**y**'));
      Prints **-1** on the console
   d) System.debug(s.indexOf(' '));
      Prints **5** on the console

7. String s = 'Apex is Apex';
   Which ones are true?
   a) System.debug(s.lastIndexOf('**e**'));
      Prints **2** on the console
   b) System.debug(s.lastIndexOf('**pex**'));
      Prints **9** on the console
   c) System.debug(s.toUpperCase().lastIndexOf('**X**'));
      Prints **3** on the console
   d) System.debug(s.toLowerCase().lastIndexOf('**a**'));
      Prints **8** on the console

8. String s = 'Learn';
   String t = 'Apex';
   Which one is false?
   a) System.debug((s+t).length());
      Prints **9** on the console
   b) System.debug(s.length()+t.length());
      Prints **9** on the console
   c) System.debug(s+t.length());
      Prints **Learn4** on the console
   d) None

9. String s = ' Apex Is Easy   ';
   Which ones are **false**?
   a) String result = s.deleteWhiteSpace();
      System.debug(result);
      Prints **ApexIsEasy** on the console
   b) String result = s.trim();
      System.debug(result);
      Prints **Apex Is Easy** on the console
   c) Integer result = s.trim().length();
      System.debug(result);
      Prints **10** on the console
   d) Integer result = s.deleteWhiteSpace().length();
      System.debug(result);
      Prints **12** on the console

10. String s = 'Study hard';
Which <u>ones</u> are true?
a) System.debug(s.substring(6));
   Prints **hard** on the console.
b) System.debug(s.substring(0));
   Prints **S** on the console.
c) String s = 'Study hard';
   System.debug(s.substring(0).equals(s));
   Prints **false** on the console.
d) System.debug(s.substring(9));
   Prints **d** on the console.

11. Which <u>ones</u> are true?

a) String s = 'Learn Apex';
   System.debug(s.substring(1,5));
   Prints **earn** on the console
b) String s = 'Learn Apex';
   System.debug(s.substring(0,1));
   Prints **L** on the console
c) String s = 'Learn Apex';
   System.debug(s.substring(9,10));
   Prints **x** on the console
d) String s = 'Learn Apex';
   System.debug(s.substring(9,6));
   Prints **Ape** on the console

12. If *name* is a String variable then which <u>ones</u> are true?
a) *name*.*indexOf('m')* equals to *name*.*lastIndexOf('m')* then *m* is a unique character in the *name* String.
b) *name*.*deleteWhiteSpace()*.*length()* equals to *name*.*length()* then the *name* String does not have any space character in it.
c) *name*.*length()* equals to zero then *name*.*indexOf()* returns *-1* for all characters
d) String s = *name*.*trim()*;
   String t = *name*.*deleteWhiteSpace()*;
   If *t.length()* is less than *s.length()* then s has at least one space character in the middle of the String.

13. Which <u>ones</u> are true?
- a) String str = '**Hello World!**';
  System.debug(str.length() **>** str.charAt(6));
  Prints false on the console.
- b) String str = '**Hello!**';
  System.debug(str.contains('**E**') **!=** str.equalsIgnoreCase('**HELLO!**'));
  Prints true on the console.
- c) String str = '**Hello Oscar!**';
  System.debug(str.charAt(4) **==** str.charAt(6));
  Prints true on the console.
- d) String str = '**Hello Tom!**';
  System.debug(str.countMatches('**l**') **==** str.countMatches('**o**'));
  Prints true on the console.

14. Which <u>ones</u> are **false**?
- a) String str = '**Hello World!**';
  System.debug(str.toLowerCase().contains('**world**'));
  Prints true on the console.
- b) String str1 = '**Hello**';
  String str2 = '**HELLO**';
  System.debug(str1.equals(str2.toLowerCase().capitalize()));
  Prints true on the console.
- c) String str = '**Java**';
  System.debug(str.replace('**e**', '**i**'));
  Prints **Jiva** on the console.
- d) String str = '**Apex**';
  System.debug(str.replace('**A**', '**e**'));
  Prints **ApAx** on the console.

15. Which one is true?
- a) String str = '**Learn Apex, earn money**';
  System.debug(str.replace('**earn**', '**?**'));
  Gives Compile Time Error because instead of 4 characters you **cannot** replace
  1 character.
- b) String str = '**Learn Apex, earn money**';
  System.debug(str.replace('**earn**', '**?**'));
  Prints **Learn Apex, ? money** on the console
- c) String str = '**Learn Apex, earn money**';
  System.debug(str.replace('**n**', ''));
  Prints **Lear Apex, ear moey** on the console
- d) String str = '**Teach more, learn more**';
  System.debug(str.replace('**more**', '**less**'));
  Prints **Teach less, learn more** on the console

16. Which one is <u>false</u>?

  a) String str = '1a 2B-';
     String result = str.replaceAll('[^0-9]', '');
     System.debug(result);
     Prints **12** on the console

  b) String str = '1a 2B-';
     String result = str.replaceAll('[a-z]', '');
     System.debug(result);
     Prints **1 2-** on the console

  c) String str = '1a 2B-';
     String result = str.replaceAll('[ ]','');
     System.debug(result);
     Prints **1a2B-** on the console

  d) String str = '1a 2B-';
     String result = str.replaceAll('[^]', '*');
     System.debug(result);
     Prints **** ***** on the console

17. Which <u>ones</u> are true?

  a) String **s** = 'Ali Can';
     Boolean result = **s**.*containsIgnoreCase(*'ALI'*)*;
     System.debug(result);
     Prints **true** on the console

  b) String **s** = 'Canan Canan';
     String result = **s**.*remove(*'Can'*)*;
     System.debug(result);
     Prints **an an** on the console

  c) String **s** = 'Canan Canan';
     String **t** = **s**.*remove(*'an'*)*;
     String **u** = **s**.replace('an','');
     Boolean result = **t**.equals(**u**);
     System.debug(result);
     Prints **true** on the console

  d) String **s** = 'Canan Can';
     String result = **s**.*remove(*'n'*).replace(*'a','*'*)*;
     System.debug(result);
     Prints **C** C*** on the console

18. Which one is <u>false</u>?

a) String **s** = '$15.99';
String **t** = s.remove('$');
Decimal **u** = Decimal.valueOf(**t**);
System.debug(**u** + 5);
Prints **20.99** on the console

b) String **s** = 'I am 15 years old';
String **t** = **s**.replaceAll('[^0-9]','');
Integer **u** = Integer.valueOf(**t**);
System.debug(**u** + 5);
Prints **20** on the console

c) String s = 'abc@gmail.com';
String t = s.remove('.com').split('@')[1];
System.debug(t);
Prints **gmail** on the console

d) The value of **indexOf()** can be greater than the value of **lastIndexOf()**

DATE CLASS

1. Current date is the 14th of November 2021. If you want to create a Date variable whose value is the same as the current date, which codes can you type?
   a) Date currentDate = Date.today();
   b) Date currentDate = Date.newInstance(2021, 11, 14);
   c) Date currentDate = Date.newInstance(2021, 10, 9);
      currentDate = currentDate.addMonths(1).addDays(5);
   d) Date currentDate = Date.currentDate();

2. If the current date is the 14th of November 2021, which <u>ones</u> print *true* on the console?
   a) Date currentDate = Date.today();
      Date dueDate = Date.newInstance(2021, 11, 14);
      Boolean result = currentDate.isSameDay(dueDate);
      System.debug(result);
   b) Date currentDate = Date.today();
      Date dueDate = Date.newInstance(2021, 11, 14);
      Boolean result = dueDate.isSameDay(currentDate);
      System.debug(result);
   c) Date currentDate = 11/14/2021;
      Date dueDate = Date.newInstance(2021, 11, 14);
      Boolean result = dueDate.isSameDay(currentDate);
      System.debug(result);
   d) Date currentDate = Date.today();
      Date dueDate = 11/14/2021;
      Boolean result = dueDate.isSameDay(currentDate);
      System.debug(result);

3. Which <u>ones</u> are true?
   a) Date myDate = Date.parse('12/27/2009');
      System.debug(myDate);
      The output is *2009-12-27 00:00:00*
   b) Date myDate = Date.parse('27/12/2009');
      System.debug(myDate);
      The code gives error
   c) Date myDate = Date.parse(12/27/2009);
      System.debug(myDate);
      The code gives error
   d) None

4. Which one is true?
   a) Date myDate = Date.today();
      String y = myDate.year();
      System.debug(y);
      Prints **2022** on the console.
   b) Date myDate = Date.today();
      Integer m = myDate.month();
      Integer d = myDate.day();
      System.debug(m+d) ;
      Prints **29** on the console.
   c) Date **d** = currentDate.addYears(3).addMonths(-4);
      Date **e** = currentDate.addMonths(32);
      System.debug(**d**.*isSameDay(***e***)*);
      Prints **false** on the console
   d) None

5. Date d = Date.newInstance(2000, 8, 21);
   Date e = Date.newInstance(2015, 8, 21);
   Which one is <u>false</u>?
   a) Date **d** = Date.newInstance(2000, 8, 21);
      Date **e** = Date.newInstance(2001, 8, 25);
      Integer **n** = **d**.daysBetween(**e**);
      System.debug(**n**);
      Prints **369** on the console.
   b) Date **d** = Date.newInstance(2000, 8, 21);
      Date **e** = Date.newInstance(2001, 8, 25);
      Integer **n** = **e**.daysBetween(**d**);
      System.debug(**n**);
      Prints **369** on the console.
   c) Date **d** = Date.newInstance(2000, 8, 21);
      Date **e** = Date.newInstance(2000, 8, 21);
      Integer **n** = **e**.daysBetween(**d**);
      System.debug(**n**);
      Prints **0** on the console.
   d) None

6. String **s** = 'Atlanta';
   Integer a = **s**.charAt(0);
   Integer b = **s**.charAt(**s**.length()-1);
   System.debug(a+b);
   What is the output?
   a) Aa
   b) The sum of the ASCII values of 'A' and 'a'
   c) The sum of the ASCII values of 'A' and 't'
   d) Gives error

7. String **s** = 'Alabama';
   Boolean a = **s**.startsWith('A');
   Boolean b = **s**.endsWithIgnoreCase('A');
   System.debug(a && b);
   What is the output?
   a) true
   b) false
   c) null
   d) Gives error

8. Which <u>ones</u> print **true** on the console?
   a) System.debug(**!false**);
   b) Integer **a** = 12;
      Integer **b** = 13;
      System.debug(**a!=b**);
   c) System.debug(**!(!true)**);
   d) String **s** = '*Alabama*';
      String **t** = **s**.toLowerCase();
      Integer **a** = **t**.charAt(0);
      Integer **b** = **t**.charAt(**t**.length()-1);
      System.debug(**a!=b**);

DATE - TIME CLASS

1. Which ones are true?
   a) **HH: mm** format uses a 24-hour clock system
   b) **hh: mm a** format uses a 12-hour clock system and displays AM or PM
   c) **hh: mm** format uses a 12-hour clock system and does not display AM or PM
   d) **HH: MM** is the wrong format because we use uppercase **M**s for months

2. Which ones are true?
   a) Following code Prints **GMT DateTime** on the console
      DateTime myDateTime = DateTime.now();
      System.debug(myDateTime);
   b) *If you live in the* USA following code gives error
      Date **dt** = Date.parse('14/10/2011');
   c) *If you live in the USA* following code Prints 25 on the console
      Date **dt** = Date.newInstance(2022, 11, 25);
      System.debug(**dt**.format().substring(3, 5));
   d) Following code masks the year component with ****
      Date **myDate** = Date.newInstance(2022, 3, 26);
      String *stringDate* = **myDate**.format();
      Integer year = myDate.year();
      String yearMasked = *stringDate*.replace(String.valueOf(year), '****');

3. Which one is false?
   a) DateTime dt = DateTime.newInstance(2002, 11, 21, 14, 2, 2);
      System.debug(dt.time());
      Prints **14:02:02.000Z** on the console
   b) In 14:02:02.000Z, '**Z**' indicates UTC timezone
   c) DateTime **dt** = DateTime.newInstance(2007, 6, 23, 3, 3, 3);
      dt.*getTime();* returns the the number of milliseconds since January 1, 1970, 00:00:00 GMT represented by **dt**
   d) None

IF STATEMENT

1. Which ones are true?
   a) ```
      Integer a = 0;
      if(a >= 0) {
          System.debug('Good');
      }
      if(a <= 0) {
          System.debug('Bad');
      }
      ```
      The output is
      **Good**
      **Bad**
   b) ```
      String s = 'Apex';
      if(s.contains('a')) {
          System.debug('Good');
      }else if(s.length()==4) {
          System.debug('Bad');
      }
      ```
      The output is
      Bad
   c) ```
      if(3>2 && 4<7) {
          System.debug('Good');
      }
      if(3<2 || 4<7) {
          System.debug('Bad');
      }
      ```
      The output is
      **Good**
   d) ```
      Integer num = 12;
      if(Math.mod(num, 2)!=0){
          System.debug('Good');
      }
      System.debug('Done!');
      ```
      The output is
      Done!

2. Integer x = 12;
   Integer y = 10;
   if(Math.mod(x, 3)!=0 && Math.mod(y, 5)==0){
       System.debug('Good');
   }else if(Math.mod(x, 3)!=0 || Math.mod(y, 5)==0){
       System.debug('Bad');
   }else{
       System.debug('Ugly');
   }
   What is the output?
   a) Good
   b) Bad
   c) Ugly
   d) Nothing

3. if(age<0) {
       System.debug('Negative ages are not valid');
   }else if(age<30) {
       System.debug('Young');
   }else if(age<=50) {
       System.debug('Middle age');
   }else if(age<=70) {
       System.debug('Old');
   }else if(age>70) {
       System.debug('Senior');
   }else{
       System.debug('The oldest');
   }
   Which one is <u>false</u>?
   a) If the age is **50** then the output is **Middle age**
   b) If age is **170** then output is **The oldest**
   c) If the age is **72** then the output is **Senior**
   d) If the age is **69** then the output is **Old**

4. String s = 'Apex Apex';
```
String s = 'Apex Apex';
if(s.indexOf('A')==1){
    if(s.lastIndexOf('e')==7){
    System.debug('Better');
}else{
    System.debug('Good');
}
}else{
    if(s.substring(6).equals('pex')){
    System.debug('Bad');
}else{
    System.debug('Ugly');
    }
}
```
What is the output?
a) Better
b) Good
c) Bad
d) Ugly

5. String stateAbbreviation = 'F3!';
```
String stateAbbreviation = 'F3!';
if(stateAbbreviation.length()>2){
    System.debug('Good');
}
if(stateAbbreviation.replaceAll('[^a-z]','').length()!=0){
    System.debug('Bad');
}
if(stateAbbreviation.replaceAll('[^A-Za-z]','').length()!=0){
    System.debug('Ugly');
}
if(stateAbbreviation.replaceAll('\\W','').length()!=0){
    System.debug('Worst');
}
```
Which one is not the output?
a) Good
b) Bad
c) Ugly
d) Worst

6.
```
if(operator.equals('+')) {
    System.debug(a+b);
}else if(operator.equals('-')){
    System.debug(a-b);
}else if(operator.equals('*')){
    System.debug(a*b);
}else if(operator.equals('/')){
    System.debug(a/b);
}else if(operator.equals('%')){
    System.debug(a*b/100);
}else{
    System.debug('Invalid operator');
}
```
For the given code which <u>ones</u> are <u>false</u>?

a) Integer a = 2;
   Integer b = 3;
   String operator = '+';
   The output is 5

b) Integer a = 20;
   Integer b = 30;
   String operator = '-';
   The output is 10

c) Integer a = 20;
   Integer b = 30;
   String operator = '%';
   The output is 6

d) Integer a = 3;
   Integer b = 5;
   String operator = 'x';
   The output is 15

7. Which one of the following Prints the **first digit** and the **last digit** of the variable **x**?
   a) Integer **x** = 7342;
      Integer lastDigit = Math.mod(**x**,10);
      Integer firstDigit = **x**/1000;
      System.debug(firstDigit);
      System.debug(lastDigit);
   b) Integer **x** = 7342;
      Integer lastDigit = Math.mod(**x**,1000);
      Integer firstDigit = **x**/10;
      System.debug(firstDigit);
      System.debug(lastDigit);
   c) Integer **x** = 7342;
      Integer lastDigit = Math.mod(**x**,10);
      Integer firstDigit = **x**/100;
      System.debug(firstDigit);
      System.debug(lastDigit);
   d) Integer **x** = 7342;
      Integer lastDigit = Math.mod(**x**,10);
      Integer firstDigit = **x**/10;
      System.debug(firstDigit);
      System.debug(lastDigit);

8.
```
if(Math.mod(x,3) == 0){
    System.debug('The number is divisible by 3');
}else if(Math.mod(x,3) == 1){
    System.debug('The number is not divisible by 3, the remainder is 1');
}else{
    System.debug('The number is not divisible by 3, the remainder is 2');
}
```
Which one is <u>false</u> for the given code snippet?
   a) Gives Error
   b) If x = 9 then the output is **The number is divisible by 3**
   c) If x = 22 then the output is **The number is not divisible by 3, the remainder is 1**
   d) If x = 32 then the output is **The number is not divisible by 3, the remainder is 2**

TERNARY STATEMENT

1. String a = 'Apex';
    String b = 'APEX';
    if(a.equals(b)) {
        System.debug('Good');
    }else {
        System.debug('Bad');
    }
    Which <u>ones</u> have the same output?
    a) String a = 'Apex';
        String b = 'APEX';
        String result = a.equalsIgnoreCase(b) ? 'Bad' : 'Good';
        System.debug(Result);
    b) String a = 'Apex';
        String b = 'APEX';
        String result = a.equalsIgnoreCase(b) ? 'Good' : 'Bad';
        System.debug(Result);
    c) String a = 'Apex';
        String b = 'APEX';
        String result = a.equals(b) ? 'Bad' : 'Good';
        System.debug(Result);
    d) String a = 'Apex';
        String b = 'APEX';
        String result = a.equals(b) ? 'Good' : 'Bad';
        System.debug(Result);

2. Integer i = -75;
    String result = i>9 && i<100 ? '2 digits' : 'Not 2 digits';
    System.debug(result);
    What is the output?
    a) 2 digits
    b) Not 2 digits
    c) Nothing on the console
    d) Gives error

3. Which one is <u>false</u>?
   a) Integer y = 11;
      Integer x = y>5 ? 3*y : 4*y;
      System.debug(x);
      Prints **33** on the console
   b) Integer y = 5;
      Integer x = y>5 ? 3*y : 4*y;
      System.debug(x);
      Prints **20** on the console
   c) Integer y = 0;
      Integer x = y>5 ? 3*y : 4*y;
      System.debug(x);
      Prints **0** on the console
   d) None

4. Which one is <u>false</u>?
   a) Integer y = 10;
      Boolean result = Math.mod(y, 2)==0||y<13 ? true : (y<0 ? true : false);
      System.debug(result);
      Prints **true** on the console
   b) Integer y = -12;
      Boolean result = Math.mod(y, 2)==0||y<13 ? true : (y<0 ? true : false);
      System.debug(result);
      Prints **true** on the console
   c) Integer y = 15;
      Boolean result = Math.mod(y, 2)==0||y<13 ? true : (y<0 ? true : false);
      System.debug(result);
      Prints **false** on the console
   d) Integer y = -17;
      Boolean result = Math.mod(y, 2)==0||y<13 ? true : (y<0 ? true : false);
      System.debug(result);
      Prints **false** on the console

5. Integer x = (y > 5) ? (y<10 ? 2+y : 3*y) : (y>10 ? 2*y : 3+y);
   System.debug(x);
   Which <u>ones</u> are true?
   a) If y = 10 then the value of x is 30
   b) If y = 4 then the value of x is 8
   c) If y = 11 then the value of x is 13
   d) If y = 1 then the value of x is 4

6. String result = **s**.length()>**t**.length() ? **s** : **t**;
   System.debug(result);
   Which one is <u>false</u>?
   a) String **s** = 'Good';
      String **t** = 'Bad';
      The output is **Good**
   b) String **s** = 'Good';
      String **t** = 'Ugly';
      The output is **Ugly**
   c) String **s** = ' ';
      String **t** = '';
      The output is *space character*
   d) String **s** = '';
      String **t** = '';
      Gives error

SWITCH STATEMENT

1. String monthName = 'June';
   switch on monthName{
       when 'december', 'january', 'february'{
       System.debug('Winter');
       }
   when 'march', 'april', 'may'{
       System.debug('Spring');
       }
   when 'june', 'july', 'august'{
       System.debug('Summer');
       }
   when 'september', 'october', 'november'{
       System.debug('Summer');
       }
   when else{
       System.debug('Invalid month name');
       }
   }
   What is the output?
   a) Summer
   b) Invalid month name
   c) Nothing
   d) Gives error

2. Which <u>ones</u> are true?
   a) *global* access modifier means the method or variable can be used by any Apex code that has access to the class, not just the Apex code in the same application.
   b) **protected** access modifier means that the method or variable is visible to any inner classes in the defining Apex class, and to the classes that extend the defining Apex class.
   c) *public* access modifier means the method or variable can be used by any Apex in this application.
   d) **private** access modifier means that the method or variable is accessible only within the Apex class in which it is defined.

3.
```
switch on dayName{
    when 'Saturday'{
        if(isOff){
            System.debug('I am not working');
        }else{
            System.debug('I should work');
        }
    }
    when 'Sunday'{
        String result = isOff ? 'I should not have accepted to work' : 'I do not work on Sundays';
        System.debug(result);
    }
    when else{
        System.debug(dayName + ' is not weekend day name');
    }
}
```
Which one is <u>false</u>?

a) If
   String dayName = 'Saturday';
   Boolean isOff = true;
   then the output is **I am not working**

b) If
   String dayName = 'Sunday';
   Boolean isOff = false;
   then the output is **I do not work on Sundays**

c) If
   String dayName = 'Friday';
   Boolean isOff = false;
   then the output is **Friday is not weekend day name**

d) None

4.
```
switch on d.toLowerCase(){
    when 'sunday'{
        System.debug(1);
    }
    when 'monday'{
        System.debug(2);
    }
    when 'tuesday'{
        System.debug(3);
    }
    when 'wednesday'{
        System.debug(4);
    }
    when 'thursday'{
        System.debug(5);
    }
    when 'friday'{
        System.debug(6);
    }
    when 'saturday'{
        System.debug(7);
    }
}
```
Which one is <u>false</u>?
a) For **String d = 'Monday';**
   Nothing will be printed on the console
b) For **String d = 'tuesday';**
   3 will be printed on the console
c) For **String d = 'SATURDAY';**
   7 will be printed on the console
d) For **String d = 'HOLIDAY';**
   Nothing will be printed on the console

5.
```
switch on Math.mod(num, 10){
    when 0, 2, 4, 6, 8{
        System.debug('Even');
    }
    when 1, 3, 5, 7, 9{
        System.debug('Odd');
    }
    when else{
        System.debug('Not digit');
    }
}
```
Which one is <u>false</u>?
a) No need to type the "**when else**" part
b) For **Integer = 24;**
   Even will be printed on the console
c) For **Integer = 13;**
   Odd will be printed on the console
d) *Note: ASCII Value of 'A' is 65*
   For **Integer = 'A'.charAt(1);**
   Odd will be printed on the console

6. *Note 1: **getRandomNumber()** method returns one of the 0, 1, 2, 3, 4, 5, 6 randomly.*
   *Note 2: **getRandomNumber()** method was created inside the Number Class.*
   *Note 3: **getRandomNumber()** method is a **static method***

```
switch on Number.getRandomNumber(){
    when 0, 1, 2{
        System.debug('It is less than three');
    }
    when 3{
        System.debug('It is three');
    }
    when 4, 5, 6{
        System.debug('It is more than three');
    }
    when else{
        System.debug('I do not know this');
    }
}
```
Which <u>ones</u> are true for the given code?
a) ***getRandomNumber()*** method is a ***static method*** because of that it must be used with the class name
b) If ***getRandomNumber()*** method returns 1, the output will be ***It is less than three***
c) If ***getRandomNumber()*** method returns a number which is more than 3, the output will be ***It is more than three***
d) If ***getRandomNumber()*** method returns a number which is less than or equal to 3, the output can be ***It is three*** or ***It is less than three***

FOR LOOP

1. ```
   for ( Integer j = 10;  j >0;  j++){
        System.debug('Hello');
   }
   ```
   How many times is **Hello** printed on the console?
   a) 10
   b) 11
   c) 0
   d) Infinitely many times

2. ```
   Integer y = 1;
   for (Integer i = 0; i<4; i++) {
        y = y + i;
   }
   System.debug(y);
   ```
   What is the output?
   a) 5
   b) 6
   c) 7
   d) 8

3. ```
   String s = 'Marra';
   for(Integer i = s.length()-1; i >= 0 ; i--){
        String c = s.substring(i, i+1);
        if(s.indexOf(c)==s.lastIndexOf(c)){
        System.debug(c);
        }
   }
   ```
   What is the output?
   a) arra
   b) M
   c) ar
   d) Mar
   ```

4. String s = 'Apex';
   String result = '';
   for(Integer i = s.length()-1; i >= 0 ; i--){
       result = result + s.substring(i, i+1);
   }
   System.debug(result);
   What is the output?
   a) xepA
   b) Apex
   c) epA
   d) Ape

5. String result = '';
   for(Integer i=1; i<4; i++) {
   for(Integer j=(5-i); j>1; j--) {
       result = result + (i+j);
   }
   System.debug(result);
   result = '';
   }
   What is the output?
   a) 543
      54
      5
   b) 432
      43
      4
   c) 5
      4
      3
   d) 4
      3
      2

WHILE LOOP

1. Integer i=1;
   Integer product=1;
   while(i<=4) {
       product = product * i;
       i++;
       System.debug(product);
   }
   What is the output?
   a) 1
      2
      6
      24
   b) 1
      2
      6
   c) 24
      6
   d) 2
      6
      24

2. Integer m = 10;
   Integer n = 2;
   Integer sum = 0;
   while(m > n) {
       m--;
       n = n + 2;
       sum = sum + m + n;
   }
   System.debug(sum);
   What is the output?
   a) 42
   b) 40
   c) 44
   d) 46

3. String s = 'Apex is Apex';
   Integer i = 0;
   String t = '';
   while(i<s.length()){
      String ch = s.substring(i, i+1);
      Boolean m = ch.equalsIgnoreCase('a') || ch.equalsIgnoreCase('e') ||
   ch.equalsIgnoreCase('i');
      if(m){
         t = t + ch;
      }
      i++;
   }
   System.debug(t);
   What is the output?
   a) AeiAe
   b) eie
   c) Aei
   d) AA

4. String s = 'HELLO';
   Integer i = 0;
   String t = '';
   while(i<s.length()){
      if(s.countMatches(s.substring(i, i+1))==1){
         t = t + s.substring(i, i+1);
      }
      i++;
   }
   System.debug(t);
   What is the output?
   a) LL
   b) HEO
   c) HELO
   d) Gives Error

5.
```
Integer j=1;
while(j<=10) {
    System.debug(j + ' ');
    j++;
}
```
Which one of the following has the same output as the given code?

a)
```
Integer j=1;
while(j<11) {
        System.debug(j + ' ');
        j++;
}
```
b)
```
Integer j=1;
while(j<10) {
        System.debug(j + ' ');
        j++;
}
```
c)
```
Integer j=10;
while(j>=1) {
        System.debug(j + ' ');
        j++;
}
```
d)
```
Integer j=10;
while(j>=1) {
        System.debug(j + ' ');
        j--;
}
```

1. Integer num=0;
   do {
      if(Math.mod(num, 2)==0){
        num += 2;
      }
   }while(num<7);
   System.debug(num);
   What is the output?
   a) 10
   b) 4
   c) 6
   d) 8

2. Which one gives a different output from the others?
   a) Integer i = 1;
      while(i<1){
              System.debug('Hi');
              i++;
      }
   b) Integer k = 1;
      do{
              System.debug('Hi');
              k++;
      }while(k<1);
   c) for(Integer i=1; i<1; i++){
              System.debug('Hi');
      }
   d) All give the same output

3. Integer i = 758;
   Integer s = 0;
   do{
      s = s + Math.mod(i, 10);
      i = i/10;
   }while(i!=0);
   System.debug(s);
   What is the output?
   a) 8
   b) 13
   c) 15
   d) 20

4.
```
Integer num = 1;
do {
    System.debug(num + ' ');
    num++;
}while(num<2);
```
Which output is the same as the given program's output?

a)
```
Integer num = 1;
while(num<2) {
    System.debug(num + ' ');
    num = num + 1;
}
```

b)
```
Integer num = 1;
while(num<=1) {
    System.debug(num + ' ');
    num++;
}
```

c)
```
for(Integer i=1; i<2; i++){
    System.debug(i + ' ');
}
```

d) All give the same output

5.
```
Integer num = 2;
do {
    System.debug(num + ' ');
    num++;
}while(num>2);
```
Which one is true for the given code?

a) The program does not run
b) Infinite loop
c) Prints 2 on the console
d) Prints nothing on the console

ARRAYS

1. Which one is true?
   a) Integer[] ages = new Integer[3];
      ages[1] = 10;
      ages[2] = 15;
      ages[3] = 23;
   b) Integer[] ages = new Integer[3];
      ages[0] = 3;
      ages[1] = 3.5;
      ages[2] = 4;
   c) Integer[] ages = new Integer[3];
      ages[0] = 3;
      ages[1] = 4;
   d) Integer[] ages = new Integer[3];
      ages[0] = 10;
      ages[1] = 15;
      ages[2] = 23;
      ages[3] = 28;

2. Which ones are false?
   a) Integer[] arr = new Integer[]{5, 9, 6, 10, 3};
      System.debug(arr);
      Prints **(5, 9, 6, 10, 3)** on the console
   b) Integer[] arr = new Integer[]{5, 9, 6, 10, 3};
      System.debug(arr[1] + arr[2]);
      Prints **14** on the console
   c) Integer[] arr = new Integer[]{5, 9, 6, 10, 3};
      System.debug(arr[*arr.length()-1*]);
      Prints **3** on the console
   d) None

3. **Note:** *The **continue** keyword is used to end the current iteration in a loop, and continues to the next iteration.*

```
String[] arr = new String[]{'Ali', 'Mary', 'Tom', 'Brad'};
for(Integer i=0; i<arr.size(); i++){
    if(i==2){
        continue;
    }
    System.debug(arr[i]);
}
```

What is the output?

a) Ali
   Mary
   Brad
b) Tom
c) Ali
   Mary
d) Tom
   Brad

4. **Note:** *The **break** keyword is used to break out a loop, a loop*

```
String[] arr = new String[]{'Ali', 'Mary', 'Tom', 'Brad'};
for(Integer i=0; i<arr.size(); i++){
    if(i==2){
        break;
    }
    System.debug(arr[i]);
}
```

What is the output?

a) Ali
   Mary
b) Tom
   Brad
c) Tom
d) Ali
   Mary
   Brad

5. String[] arr = new String[]{'Ali', 'Mary', 'Tom Hanks', 'Brad Pitt'};
   Which <u>ones</u> give the total number of characters of the array elements?
   a) Integer sum = 0;
      ```
      for(Integer i=0; i<arr.size(); i++){
             sum = sum + arr[i].length();
      }
      System.debug(sum);
      ```
   b) String[] arr = new String[]{'Ali', 'Mary', 'Tom Hanks', 'Brad Pitt'};
      ```
      Integer sum = 0;
      for(String w : arr){
             sum = sum + w.length();
      }
      System.debug(sum);
      ```
   c) String[] arr = new String[]{'Ali', 'Mary', 'Tom Hanks', 'Brad Pitt'};
      ```
      Integer i = 0;
      Integer sum = 0;
      while(i<arr.size()){
             sum = sum + arr[i].length();
                i++;
      }
      System.debug(sum);
      ```
   d) String[] arr = new String[]{'Ali', 'Mary', 'Tom Hanks', 'Brad Pitt'};
      ```
      Integer i = 0;
      Integer sum = 0;
      do{
             sum = sum + arr[i].length();
      }while(i<arr.size());
      System.debug(sum);
      ```

FOR-EACH LOOP

1.
```
String[] arr = new String[]{'Ali', 'Mary', 'Tom', 'Brad'};
for(String w : arr){
    String f = w.substring(0, 1);

    Integer g = w.length()-1;
    String h = w.substring(g, g+1);

    System.debug(f + h);
}
```
What is the output?
a) Gives error
b) A
   M
   T
   B
c) I
   Y
   m
   d
d) Ai
   My
   Tm
   Bd

2.
```
String[] arr = new String[]{'Ali', 'Mary', 'Tom', 'Brad'};
for(String w : arr){
    System.debug(w + '=' + w.length());
    if(w.equals('Tom')){
        break;
    }
}
```
What is the output?
a) Ali=3
   Mary=4
   Tom=3
b) Ali=3
   Mary=4
c) Brad=4
d) Tom=3
   Brad=4

3.
```
Integer[] arr = new Integer[]{5, 9, 6, 10, 3};
Integer x = arr[0];
for(Integer w : arr){
   x = Math.max(x, w);
}
Integer y = arr[0];
for(Integer w : arr){
   y = Math.min(y, w);
}
System.debug(x - y);
```
What is the output?
a) 7
b) 10
c) 3
d) 13

4.
```
Integer[] arr = new Integer[]{5, 9, 6, 10, 3};
Integer x = 0;
for(Integer w : arr){
   if(Math.mod(w, 2)==0){
     continue;
   }
   x = x + w;
}
System.debug(x);
```
What is the output?
a) 17
b) 16
c) 25
d) 14

5.
```
Integer[] arr = new Integer[]{5, 9, 6};
for(Integer w : arr){
    for(Integer k : arr){
        if(w>=k){
            continue;
        }
        System.debug(w + k);
    }
}
```
What is the output?

a) 10
   14
   11
   18

b) 14
   11
   14
   15

c) 14
   15
   12

d) 14
   11
   15

LISTS

1. List<String> myList = new List<String>() ;
   myList.add('A');
   myList.add('B');
   myList.add('C');
   myList.add('D');
   Which one is <u>false</u>?
   a) System.debug(myList);
      Prints **(A, B, C, D)** on the console
   b) myList.add(2, 'X');
      System.debug(myList);
      Prints **(A, B, X, C, D)** on the console
   c) myList.remove(1);
      System.debug(myList);
      Prints **(A, X, C, D)** on the console
   d) System.debug(myList.get(4));
      Prints **D** on the console

2. Integer[] arr = new Integer[]{5, 3, 2, 3, 2};
   List<Integer> myList = new List<Integer>();

   for(Integer w : arr){
     if(!myList.contains(w)){
       myList.add(w);
     }
   }
   System.debug(myList);
   What is the output?
   a) (5, 3, 2, 3, 2)
   b) (5, 3, 2)
   c) (3, 2)
   d) (5)

3.
```
List<Integer> myList = new List<Integer>();

for(Integer i=5; i<9; i++){
    myList.clear();
    myList.add(i);
}
System.debug(myList);
```
What is the output?
a) (5, 6, 7, 8)
b) (8)
c) (5)
d) (6, 7)

4.
```
List<Integer> myList = new List<Integer>();
myList.add(5);
myList.add(6);
myList.add(10);

Integer m = 1;
for(Integer w : myList){
    m = m * w;
}
System.debug(m);
```
What is the output?
a) 21
b) 0
c) 300
d) 1

5.
```
List<String> myList = new List<String>();
myList.add('K');
myList.add('M');
myList.add('N');
myList.add('L');
```
Which one is false?
a) myList.set(myList.size()-1, 'Z');
   Changes the last element to **Z**
b) myList.set(0, 'A');
   Changes the first element to **A**
c) myList.indexOf('L');
   Returns the index of first occurrence of **L**
d) myList.sort();
   Orders the list elements in descending order

6.  ```apex
    List<String> myList = new List<String>();
    myList.add('Alican');
    myList.add('Angelina');
    myList.add('Mary');
    myList.add('Kerem');

    for(Integer i = 0; i<myList.size(); i++){
       if(myList.get(i).length()>5){
          myList.remove(i);
          i--;
       }
    }
    System.debug(myList);
    ```
    What is the output?
    a) (Mary, Kerem)
    b) (Alican, Angelina)
    c) (Mary)
    d) (Alican, Angelina, Kerem)

7.  ```apex
    List<Integer> myList = new List<Integer>();
    myList.add(12);
    myList.add(84);
    myList.add(4);
    myList.add(132);
    myList.add(45);

    myList.sort();
    Integer x = myList.get(myList.size()-1);
    Integer y = myList.get(0);
    System.debug(x - y);
    ```
    What is the output?
    a) 132
    b) 4
    c) 128
    d) 136

SETS

1. Which one is false?
   a) Set<Integer> mySet = new Set<Integer>();
      mySet.add(12);
      mySet.add(84);
      mySet.add(4);
      mySet.add(12);
      System.debug(mySet);
      Prints **{12, 84, 4, 12}** on the console
   b) Set<Integer> mySet = new Set<Integer>();
      mySet.add(12);
      mySet.add(84);
      mySet.add(4);
      System.debug(mySet.contains(12));
      Prints **true** on the console
   c) Set<Integer> mySet = new Set<Integer>();
      mySet.add(12);
      mySet.add(84);
      mySet.add(4);
      mySet.remove(84);
      System.debug(mySet);
      Prints **{4, 12}** on the console
   d) Set<Integer> mySet = new Set<Integer>();
      mySet.add(12);
      mySet.add(84);
      mySet.add(4);
      mySet.clear();
      Set<Integer> yourSet = new Set<Integer>();
      System.debug(mySet.equals(yourSet));
      Prints **true** on the console

2. List<Integer> myList = new List<Integer>();
   myList.add(12);
   myList.add(84);
   myList.add(4);
   myList.add(84);
   myList.add(12);
   Set<Integer> mySet = new Set<Integer>(myList);
   System.debug(mySet);
   What is the output?
   a) {4, 12, 84, 12, 84}
   b) Gives error
   c) {}
   d) {4, 12, 84}

3.
```
Set<Integer> mySet = new Set<Integer>();
mySet.add(12);
mySet.add(84);
mySet.add(4);
mySet.add(17);
Set<Integer> yourSet = new Set<Integer>();
yourSet.add(17);
yourSet.add(84);
yourSet.add(5);
```
Which <u>ones</u> are true for the given Sets?

a) mySet.retainAll(yourSet);
   System.debug(mySet);
   Prints **{17, 84}** on the console.

b) mySet.retainAll(yourSet);
   System.debug(yourSet);
   Prints **{5, 17, 84}** on the console.

c) mySet.removeAll(yourSet);
   System.debug(mySet);
   Prints **{4, 12}** on the console.

d) System.debug(mySet.containsAll(yourSet));
   Prints **true** on the console.

4.
```
Set<String> mySet = new Set<String>();
mySet.add('Ali');
mySet.add('Mary');
mySet.add('Ali');
mySet.add('Brandon');

Integer x = 0;
for(String w : mySet){
    x = x + w.length();
}
System.debug(x);
```
What is the output?

a) 17
b) 14
c) 20
d) 11

5.
```
Set<String> mySet = new Set<String>();
mySet.add('Ali Can');
mySet.add('Mary Star');
mySet.add('Ali Tan');
mySet.add('Brandon Walker');

String t = '';
for(String w : mySet){
    Integer x = w.indexOf(' ') + 1;
    t = t + w.substring(x, x+1);
}
System.debug(t);
```
What is the output?
a) AMAB
b) CSTW
c) ACMSATBM
d) Gives error

MAPS

1. Which one is <u>false</u>?

   a) Map<String, Integer> myMap = new Map<String, Integer>();
      System.debug(myMap);
      Prints **{ }** on the console

   b) Map<String, Integer> myMap = new Map<String, Integer>();
      myMap.put('Tom', 13);
      myMap.put('Mary', 18);
      myMap.put('Tom', 25);
      Prints **{Mary=18, Tom=13, Tom=25}** on the console

   c) Map<String, Integer> myMap = new Map<String, Integer>();
      myMap.put('Tom', 13);
      myMap.put('Mary', 18);
      System.debug(myMap.keySet());
      Prints **{Mary, Tom}** on the console

   d) Map<String, Integer> myMap = new Map<String, Integer>();
      myMap.put('Tom', 13);
      myMap.put('Mary', 18);
      myMap.put('Brad', 13);
      System.debug(myMap.values());
      Prints **{13, 8, 13}** on the console

2. Map<String, String> myMap=new Map<String, String>();
   myMap.put('Tom Hanks', 'Fransa');
   myMap.put('Angelina Julie', 'Almanya');
   myMap.put('Brad Pitt', 'Canada');
   myMap.put('Mary Star', 'Ingiltere');

   Set<String> keys = myMap.keySet();
   String s = '';
   for(String w : keys){
       String a = w.substring(0, 1);
       String b = w.split(' ')[1].substring(0, 1);
       s = s + a + b + ' ';
   }
   System.debug(s);
   What is the output?

   a) F A C I
   b) Fa Aa Ac Ie
   c) TH AJ BP MS
   d) T A B M

3.  ```
    Map<String, String> myMap=new Map<String, String>();
    myMap.put('Tom Hanks', 'Fransa');
    myMap.put('Angelina Julie', 'Almanya');
    myMap.put('Brad Pitt', 'Canada');
    myMap.put('Mary Star', 'Ingiltere');

    List<String> values = myMap.values();
    String s = '';
    for(String w : values){
        Integer a = w.length();
        String b = w.substring(0,1);
        String c = w.substring(a-1,a);
        s = s + b + c + ' ';
    }
    System.debug(s);
    ```
    What is the output?
    a) F A C I
    b) T A B M
    c) TH AJ BP MS
    d) Fa Aa Ca Ie

4.  ```
    String s = 'Apex! my Apex.';
    String a = s.replaceAll('[^A-Za-z]', '');

    String[] b = a.split('');

    Map<String, Integer> m = new Map<String, Integer>();
    for(String w : b){
        Integer c = m.get(w);
        if(c==null){
            m.put(w, 1);
        }else{
            m.put(w, c+1);
        }
    }
    System.debug(m);
    ```
    What is the output?
    a) {A=2, e=2, m=1, p=2, x=2, y=1, !=1, .=1}
    b) {A=2, e=2, m=1, p=2, x=2, y=1}
    c) {A, e, m, p, x}
    d) {Apex=2, my=1}
    e)

5.
```
List<Integer> k = new List<Integer>{12, 21, 12, 13, 12, 21, 35};
Map<Integer, Integer> m = new Map<Integer, Integer>();

for(Integer w : k){
    Integer n = m.get(w);
    if(n==null){
        m.put(w, 1);
    }else{
        m.put(w, n+1);
    }
}
System.debug(m);
```
What is the output?
a) {12, 13, 21, 35}
b) {12=3, 13=1, 21=2, 35=1}
c) 81
d) {12=2, 13=1, 21=1, 35=1}

APEX QUESTIONS

VARIABLES

1) Create decimal variables for the prices of any 3 items. Print the sum of the prices on the console with a label.

SOLUTION

```
Decimal shirtPrice = 12.99;
Decimal hatPrice = 23.99;
Decimal shoesPrice = 15.99;
System.debug('Total price: ' + (shirtPrice + hatPrice + shoesPrice));
```

2) Type a code to find simple interest.
Note: *Simple interest formula = principal * rate * numberOfYear / 100*

SOLUTION

```
Integer principal = 10000, rate = 6, numberOfYear = 3;
Integer simpleInterest = principal * rate * numberOfYear/100;
System.debug('The simple interest is ' + simpleInterest);
```

3) Create a String and two Long variables. Print the sum and the multiplication of the long variables with the String on the console.

SOLUTION

```
String s = 'The sum is ';
Long a = 123;
Long b = 9123456782L;
System.debug(s + (a+b));
System.debug(s +a*b);
```

4) Create three boolean variables whose values are different and print their values in the same line with a space between two consecutive values.

SOLUTION

```
Boolean a = true;
Boolean b = false;
Boolean c = null;
System.debug(a + ' ' + b + ' ' + c);
```

5) Create 3 Decimal variables for the price of a book, notebook, and laptop.
   Print the total price of 2 books, 4 notebooks, and 3 laptops on the console

SOLUTION

```
Decimal book = 12.99, noteBook = 23.45, laptop = 34.12;
Decimal totalPrice = 2*book + 4*noteBook + 3*laptop;
System.debug('The total price is ' + totalPrice);
```

STRING MANIPULATIONS

1) Create a String variable for city names that have just a single word.
Print the city name with the initial is in uppercase and all the other characters are in lower cases on the console.

   Example
   mIAMI should be printed as Miami
   miami should be printed as Miami
   MIAMI should be printed as Miami
   mIaMi should be printed as Miami etc.

   SOLUTION

   ```
   String cityName = ' miami ';
   String updatedCityName = cityName.trim().toLowerCase().capitalize();
   System.debug(updatedCityName);
   ```

2) Create 3 String variables for people's names. Print the sum of the number of characters in all the 3 names except space characters.

   Example
   If the names are Ali Can, Merve Star, and Mark Tom you should see 22 on the console.

   SOLUTION

   ```
   String name1 = 'Ali Can';
   String name2 = 'Aliye Canan';
   String name3 = 'Aliyev Can Cananov';
   Integer NumOfChar1 = name1.deleteWhiteSpace().length();
   Integer NumOfChar2 = name2.deleteWhiteSpace().length();
   Integer NumOfChar3 = name3.deleteWhiteSpace().length();
   System.debug('Total number of characters different from space: ' + (NumOfChar1 +
   NumOfChar2 + NumOfChar3));
   ```

3) Create a String variable, print the number of characters different from space characters in the String on the console.

Example
If the String is '   Miami 33018   ' you need to print 10 on the console.

SOLUTION

```
String s2 = '   Miami 33018   ';
```
1. Way:
```
Integer numOfCharsDifferentFromSpace1 = s2.deleteWhiteSpace().length();
System.debug('Total number of non-space characters:'+numOfCharsDifferentFromSpace1);
```
2. Way:
```
Integer numOfCharsDifferentFromSpace2 = s2.replaceAll('\\s','').length();
System.debug('Total number of non-space characters:'+numOfCharsDifferentFromSpace2);
```

4) Create a String variable, print the number of non-digit characters in the String on the console.

Example
If the String is '1a3Bcf4!...' you need to print 8 on the console.

SOLUTION

```
String s1 = '2a3B4?-!5';
Integer numOfNonDigitChars = s1.replaceAll('[0-9]','').length();
System.debug('Total number of non-digit characters: ' + numOfNonDigitChars);
```

5) Create a String variable and print just the last non-space character on the console for any String.

Example
For 'Ali Can' you should print n
For 'Miami   ' you should print i etc.

SOLUTION

```
String s3 = 'Miami     ';
Integer idxOfLastNonSpace = s3.trim().length()-1;
String lastNonSpaceChar = s3.substring(idxOfLastNonSpace, idxOfLastNonSpace+1);
System.debug('The non-space last character: ' + lastNonSpaceChar);
```

6) Create a String variable and find the sum of the ASCII values of the first and the last characters of the String.

SOLUTION

```
String s4 = 'Miami';
Integer indexOfLastChar = s4.length()-1;
Integer AsciiValueOfFirstChar = s4.charAt(0);
Integer AsciiValueOfLastChar = s4.charAt(indexOfLastChar);
System.debug('Total value of the ASCII values of the first and the last character: ' +
(AsciiValueOfFirstChar + AsciiValueOfLastChar));
```

7) Create a String variable and print all characters except the first character on the console.

Example
If the String is 'Apex' you should print 'pex' on the console.

SOLUTION

```
String s5 = 'Apex';
String allCharsExceptFirstChar = s5.substring(1);
System.debug('All characters except the first character: ' + allCharsExceptFirstChar);
```

8) Create a String variable and print all characters except the last character on the console in uppercases.

Example
If the String is 'Apex' you should print 'APE' on the console.

SOLUTION

```
String s5 = 'Apex';
Integer indexOfLastChar = s5.length()-1;
String allCharsExceptLastCharInUpperCase = s5.substring(0, indexOfLastChar).
toUpperCase();
System.debug('All characters except the last character: ' +
allCharsExceptLastCharInUpperCase);
```

9) Create a String variable and print all characters except the first character and the last character on the console in uppercases.

Example
If the String is 'Apex' you should print 'PE' on the console.

SOLUTION
```
String s5 = 'Apex';
Integer indexOfLastChar = s5.length()-1;
String allCharsExceptLastCharInUpperCase = s5.substring(1, indexOfLastChar).toUpperCase();
System.debug('All characters except the first and the last character: ' + allCharsExceptLastCharInUpperCase);
```

10) Type a code to check if a String has just a single space character any position in the middle

Example
For 'Ali   Can' your code should print false on the console
For '   Ali Can   ' your code should print false on the console
For '   Ali   Can   ' your code should print false on the console
For 'Ali Can' your code should print true on the console

SOLUTION
```
String s = 'Ali Can';
String trimmedString = s.trim();
String allCharsExceptSpace = trimmedString.deleteWhiteSpace();
Boolean isThereSingleSpaceInTheMiddleAnyPosition = trimmedString.length() -
allCharsExceptSpace.length() == 1;
System.debug('Is there a single space in the middle of any position? ' +
isThereSingleSpaceInTheMiddleAnyPosition);
```

11) Type a code to check if a string does not have any space characters at the beginning and the end?

Example
For ' Ali ' your code should print false on the console
For 'Ali' your code should print true on the console

SOLUTION
```
String s = '  Ali';
String trimmedString = s.trim();
Boolean result  = s.equals(trimmedString);
System.debug('Is there space at the beginning and/or at the end? ' + !result);`
```

12) Type a code to check if a String has an uppercase initial and dot at the end.

Example
For 'Ali' your code should print false on the console
For 'ali.' your code should print false on the console
For '   Ali.   ' your code should print false on the console
For 'Ali.' your code should print true on the console
For 'ALI.' your code should print true on the console

SOLUTION

```
String s = 'Ali Can.';
Integer asciiValueOfFirstChar = s.charAt(0);
Integer asciiValueOfLastChar = s.charAt(s.length()-1);
Boolean isTheFirstCharUpper = asciiValueOfFirstChar>64 && asciiValueOfFirstChar<91;
Boolean isTheLastCharDot = asciiValueOfLastChar==46;
Boolean isFirstUpperAndLastDot = isTheFirstCharUpper && isTheLastCharDot;
System.debug('Is the first char upper and the last char dot? ' + isFirstUpperAndLastDot);
```

13) Type a code to check if a password is valid or not for the following conditions;
Password must have at least 8 characters different from the space character
Password must have at least 1 symbol

Example
For 'A2b!' your code should print false on the console
For 'A2b3cdef' your code should print false on the console
For '!1a23b4' your code should print false on the console
For '!1a23b4?es' your code should print true on the console
For '! a b 3 k' your code should print false on the console

SOLUTION

```
String pwd = '!1a23b4?es';
Boolean atLeastEightChar = pwd.deleteWhiteSpace().length()>=8;
Boolean atLeastOneSymbol = pwd.deleteWhiteSpace().replaceAll('[A-Za-z0-9]','').length()>0;
System.debug('Is the password valid? ' + (atLeastEightChar && atLeastOneSymbol));
```

14) Type code to check if a String has a specific single character or not in three different ways.

1.Way:

```
String s = 'Apex';
Boolean result = s.contains('x');
System.debug('Does the character exist? ' + result);
```

2.Way:

```
String s = 'Apex';
Boolean result =  s.countMatches('x') > 0;
System.debug('Does the character exist? ' + result);
```

2.Way:

```
String s = 'Apex';
Boolean result = s.indexOf('x') != -1;
System.debug('Does the character exist? ' + result);
```

15)
```
String shirtPrice = '$12.99';
String bookPrice = '$35.99';
```
Type code to find the sum of the shirt and book prices.

SOLUTION

```
String s =  shirtPrice.remove('$');
String b =  bookPrice.remove('$');
Decimal x = Decimal.valueOf(s);
Decimal y = Decimal.valueOf(b);
System.debug('Total price is ' + (x+y));
```

DATE CLASS

1) Type the code that finds out how many days Ali lived.
The date of birth Ali is the 12th of May 2002

   ### SOLUTION
   ```
   Date birthDateOfAli = Date.newInstance(2002, 05, 12);
   Date currentDate = Date.today();//To get current date I used today() function
   Integer theNumberOfDaysAliLived = birthDateOfAli.daysBetween(currentDate);
   System.debug('The number of days Ali lived so far is ' + theNumberOfDaysAliLived);
   ```

2) Type the code that finds out how many months Ali lived.
The date of birth Ali is the 4th of June 1997

   ### SOLUTION
   ```
   Date birthDateOfAli = Date.newInstance(1997, 06, 04);
   Date currentDate = Date.today();
   Integer numOfMonthsAliLived = birthDateOfAli.monthsBetween(currentDate);
   System.debug('The number of months Ali lived so far is ' + numOfMonthsAliLived);
   ```

3) Date of birth Ali is 4th of June 1997. Type a code to find the exact date 2 years, 3 months, and 12 days after Ali's birth date.

   ### SOLUTION
   ```
   Date birthDateOfAli = Date.newInstance(1997, 06, 04);
   Date exactDate = birthDateOfAli.addYears(2).addMonths(3).addDays(12);
   System.debug('The exact date is ' + exactDate);
   ```

4) Ali was born 45 years, 8 months, and 5 days after 29 October 1923.
Veli was born 24 years, 2 months, and 11 days before 15 September 1993.
Type a code to calculate the exact date of birth of Ali and Veli
Type a code to check if the date of birth of Ali and Veli is the same or not.

   ### SOLUTION
   ```
   Date dobAli = Date.newInstance(1923, 10, 29).addYears(45).addMonths(8).addDays(5);
   System.debug('Date of birth of Ali: ' + dobAli);
   Date dobVeli = Date.newInstance(1993, 09, 15).addYears(-24).addMonths(-2).addDays(-11);
   System.debug('Date of birth of Veli: ' + dobVeli);
   Boolean isBirthDatesSame = dobAli.isSameDay(dobVeli);
   System.debug('Are the birth dates the same? ' + isBirthDatesSame);
   ```

5) Veli was born 3 years and 11 days after Ali.
Ali gave you his date of birth as a String in the local date format.
Type a code to calculate Veli's date of birth.

SOLUTION

```
String dobAli = '11/24/2022';
Date dobAliInDateFormat = Date.parse(dateOfBirthOfAli);
Date dobVeli = dobAliInDateFormat.addYears(3).addDays(11);
System.debug('Date of birth of Veli is ' + dobVeli);
```

6) Create a Date Value for your birth date and create Date Value for your kid's birth date then calculate the difference in days.

SOLUTION

```
Date myBirthDate = Date.newInstance(1996, 8, 21);
Date myKidsBirthDate = Date.newInstance(2015, 3, 12);
Integer numberOfDays = myBirthDate.daysBetween(myKidsBirthDate);
System.debug(numberOfDays);
```

7) Get the last 2 digits of the year in the current date

SOLUTION

```
Date currentDate = Date.today();
Integer year = currentDate.year();
Integer lastTwoDigits = Math.mod(year, 100);
System.debug(lastTwoDigits);
```

8) Type a code to check if a given year is "Leap year" or not
   Leap Year:
   i) *If a year is divisible by 100 and divisible by 400 it is called a leap year. For example; 2000 is, 1900 is not*
   ii) *If a year is not divisible by 100 and divisible by 4 it is called a leap year. For example; 2004 is, 2007 is not*

SOLUTION

```
Boolean isLeap1 = Date.isLeapYear(2000);
System.debug('Is 2000 leap year? ' + isLeap1);

Boolean isLeap2 = Date.isLeapYear(1900);
System.debug('Is 2000 leap year? ' + isLeap2);
```

9) Find the sum of the month numbers of two different dates

SOLUTION

```
Date fatherBirthDate = Date.newInstance(1990, 7, 21);
Date sonBirthDate = Date.newInstance(2016, 4, 12);

Integer justMonthFather = fatherBirthDate.month();
Integer justMonthSon = sonBirthDate.month();

System.debug(justMonthFather + justMonthSon);
```

10) Find the difference in hours for two different dates

SOLUTION

```
Date fatherBirthDate = Date.newInstance(1990, 7, 21);
Date sonBirthDate = Date.newInstance(2016, 4, 12);

Integer daysBetween = fatherBirthDate.daysBetween(sonBirthDate);
System.debug(daysBetween*24);
```

DATE - TIME CLASS

1) If the hour is
   i) Between 24:00 and 05:00 then print 'Sleeping time' on the console
   ii) Between 08:00 and 16:00 then print 'Working time' on the console
   iii) Between 19:00 and 22:00 then print 'Family time' on the console
   iv) For the others print 'Personal time' on the console

   SOLUTION

```
DateTime myDateTime = DateTime.newInstance(2002, 8, 5, 7, 12, 23);
Integer hour = myDateTime.hour();

if(hour>0 && hour<5){
System.debug('Sleeping time');
}else if(hour>8 && hour<16){
System.debug('Working time');
}else if(hour>19 && hour<22){
System.debug('Family time');
}else{
System.debug('Personal time');
}
```

2) Type a code to find the time difference between Japan time zone and Germany time zone.

   SOLUTION

```
String dateTimeInJapan = DateTime.now().format('MM/d/yyyy hh:mm a', 'Japan');
System.debug('Japan Time: ' + dateTimeInJapan);

String dateTimeInGermany = DateTime.now().format('MM/d/yyyy hh:mm a', 'Germany');
System.debug('Germany Time: ' + dateTimeInGermany);

String hourInJapan = dateTimeInJapan.substring(11, 13);
Integer japanHour = Integer.valueOf(hourInJapan);
System.debug('Hour in Japan: ' + japanHour);

String hourInGermany = dateTimeInGermany.substring(11, 13);
Integer germanyHour = Integer.valueOf(hourInGermany);
System.debug('Hour in Germany: ' + germanyHour);

System.debug('If the days are same: ' + (japanHour - germanyHour));
System.debug('If the days are not same: ' + (hourInJapan + 12 - germanyHour));
```

3) Ali was born in Istanbul on the 5th of February 2015 at 10:00 am TRT, and Mark was born in the USA on the 5th of February 2015 at 12:00 pm EST. What is the difference between Ali's birth time and Mark's birth time in hours?

SOLUTION

```
DateTime aliGmt = DateTime.newInstance(2015, 2, 5, 10, 0, 0);

String aliTr = aliGmt.format('MM/dd/yyyy HH:mm a', 'Europe/Istanbul');
System.debug('Turkey: ' + aliTr);

DateTime veliGmt = DateTime.newInstance(2015, 2, 5, 12, 0, 0);

String veliNy = veliGmt.format('MM/dd/yyyy HH:mm a', 'America/New_York');
System.debug('New York: ' + veliNy);

Integer diff = Integer.valueOf(aliTr.substring(11,13))-Integer.valueOf(veliNy.substring(11,13));
System.debug('Time Difference: ' + diff);
```

4) Ali was born on the 5th of February 2015 at 10:15 am EST, and Mark was born on the 6th of March 2015 at 12:25 pm EST. Ali remained in intensive care for 23 hours and 35 minutes. Veli remained in intensive care for 1 hour and 12 minutes. What is the difference in minutes between the times Ali and Veli leave the intensive care unit?

SOLUTION

```
DateTime aliGmt = DateTime.newInstance(2015, 2, 5, 10, 1, 0).addHours(23).addMinutes(35);

Long aliEst = aliGmt.getTime();
System.debug(aliEst);

DateTime veliGmt = DateTime.newInstance(2015, 2, 6, 12, 0, 0).addHours(1).addMinutes(12);

Long veliEst = veliGmt.getTime();
System.debug(veliEst);

Long diff = veliEst - aliEst;
System.debug((diff/1000)/60);
```

5) Mark was born on 2/23/2018 at 3:15 PM GMT. What is his exact birth date and time Mark in Japan?

SOLUTION

```
Datetime markGmt = DateTime.newInstance(2018, 2, 23, 18, 23, 0);
System.debug(markGmt);
String markJst = markGmt.format('MM/dd/YYYY, HH:mm a', 'JST');
System.debug(markJst);
```

IF STATEMENT

1) Type a code to print
   a) "Winter" for December, January, February
   b) "Spring" for March, April, May
   c) "Summer" for June, July, August
   d) "Fall" for September, October, November
   e) "Invalid month name" for all the others

SOLUTION

```
String mName = 'December';
mName = mName.toLowerCase();
if(mName.equals('december') || mName.equals('january') || mName.equals('february')){
    System.debug('Winter');
}else if(mName.equals('march') || mName.equals('april') || mName.equals('may')){
    System.debug('Spring');
}else if(mName.equals('june') || mName.equals('july') || mName.equals('august')){
    System.debug('Summer');
}else    if(mName.equals('september')    ||    mName.equals('october')    ||    mName.
    equals('november'))
{
    System.debug('Fall');
}else{
    System.debug('Invalid month name');
}
```

2) Type a code to print
   a) "Valid Password" if the password has at least 8 characters different from space character
   b) "Do not use space character in password" if the password has any space character in any position
   c) "Invalid Password" if a and b conditions are not satisfied
   Note: Be careful about the orders of conditions in the solution

SOLUTION

```
String password = 'a1b2c3d4';
if(password.replaceAll('\\S','').length()>0){
    System.debug('Do not use space character in password');
}else if(password.deleteWhiteSpace().length()>=8){
    System.debug('Valid Password');
}else{
    System.debug('Invalid Password');
}
```

3) Type a code to print
   a) "Roundup by the last digit:" and print the rounded value if the last digit is greater than or equal to 5
   b) "Round down by the last digit" and print the rounded value if the last digit is less than 5

SOLUTION

```
Integer i = 124;
if(Math.mod(i, 10)>=5){
    System.debug('Round up by last digit:' + (i/10+1)*10);
}else{
    System.debug('Round down by last digit:' + (i/10)*10);
}
```

4) Type a code to print the name of the month when you entered the number of the month. For example; For 1 output is "January", for 2 output is "February" etc.

SOLUTION

```
Integer numOfMonth = 3;
if(numOfMonth==1){
    System.debug('January');
}else if(numOfMonth==2){
    System.debug('February');
}else if(numOfMonth==3){
    System.debug('March');
}else if(numOfMonth==4){
    System.debug('April');
}else if(numOfMonth==5){
    System.debug('May');
}else if(numOfMonth==6){
    System.debug('June');
}else if(numOfMonth==7){
    System.debug('July');
}else if(numOfMonth==8){
    System.debug('August');
}else if(numOfMonth==9){
    System.debug('September');
}else if(numOfMonth==10){
    System.debug('November');
}else if(numOfMonth==11){
    System.debug('October');
}else if(numOfMonth==12){
    System.debug('December');
}else{
    System.debug('Invalid month number');
}
```

5) Type a code to print
   a) "Isosceles Triangle" if two sides of a triangle are equal in length.
   b) "Equilateral Triangle" if all sides of a triangle are equal in length.
   c) "Neither isosceles, nor equilateral" if a and b conditions are not satisfied

SOLUTION

```
Integer a = 5;
Integer b = 3;
Integer c = 4;

if(a==b && b==c){
    System.debug('Equilateral Triangle');
}else if(a==b && b!=c || a==c && b!=c || b==c && a!=c){
    System.debug('Isosceles Triangle');
}else{
    System.debug('Neither isosceles, nor equilateral');
}
```

6) Type a code to create a converter that converts mile to km, second to hour, Fahrenheit to celsius. Find the formulas for conversions from Google.
   a) When a user entered 10 and mileToKm String, your code should print "16 km"(The number will be dynamic) on the console
   b) When a user entered 7200 and secondsToHours String, your code should print "2 Hours"(The number will be dynamic) on the console
   c) When user entered 83 and fahrenheitToCelsius String, your code should print "28.3333 celsius"(The number will be dynamic) on the console

SOLUTION

```
Double mile = 10;
Double seconds = 7200;
Double fahrenheit = 83;
String operator = 'fahrenheitToCelsius';

if(operator.equals('mileToKm')){
    System.debug(mile*1.60934);
}else if(operator.equals('secondsToHours')){
    System.debug((seconds/60)/60);
}else if(operator.equals('fahrenheitToCelsius')){
    System.debug((fahrenheit-32)*5/9 );
}
```

7) Type a code to check the grammatical rules for full name
   a) Your code should print "Error in initials" for "ali Can", "Ali can", "ali can"
   b) Your code should print "First name or last name missed" for single words like "Ali" or "Can" or "ali"
   c) Your code should print "Format error" for all the formats like "ALI CAN"
   d) Your code should print "Name was not entered" for one or more space characters like " " or "   "
   e) Your code should print "Invalid Name" if the name has any character different from letters and space.

   Note: If the abbreviation has more than 1 error all related error messages should be printed. For example; for "ali3" your code should print "Error in initials", "First name or the last name missed", and "Invalid Name"

SOLUTION

```apex
String fullName = 'ali Can?';

String initialOfFirstName = fullName.substring(0,1);
Integer indexOfSpace = fullName.trim().indexOf(' ');
String initialOfLastName = fullName.substring(indexOfSpace+1,indexOfSpace+2);
Boolean isFirstNameInitialUpperCase = (initialOfFirstName.charAt(0)>=65 &&
initialOfFirstName.charAt(0)<=90);
Boolean isLastNameInitialUpperCase = (initialOfLastName.charAt(0)>=65 &&
initialOfLastName.charAt(0)<=90);

if(indexOfSpace==-1){
    System.debug('First name or last name missed');
}
if(!isFirstNameInitialUpperCase || !isLastNameInitialUpperCase){
    System.debug('Error in initials');
}
if(fullName.equals(fullName.toUpperCase())){
    System.debug('Format error');
}
if(fullName.deleteWhiteSpace().length()==0){
    System.debug('Name was not entered');
}
if(fullName.deleteWhiteSpace().replaceAll('[A-Za-z]','').length()>0){
    System.debug('Invalid Name');
}
```

8) Type a code to check the format of state abbreviations in the USA
   a) Your code should print "State abbreviations cannot have more than 2 characters" if the the abbreviation has more than 2 characters
   b) Your code should print "State abbreviations cannot have lowercase characters" if the the abbreviation has lowercase characters
   c) Your code should print "State abbreviations cannot have characters different from letters" if the abbreviation has characters different from letters.

   Note: If the abbreviation has more than 1 error all related error messages should be printed. For example; for "fl3" your code should print, "State abbreviations cannot have more than 2 characters", "State abbreviations cannot have lowercase characters", and "State abbreviations cannot have characters different from letters"

   SOLUTION

```
String stateAbbreviation = 'Fl3';
if(stateAbbreviation.length()>2){
    System.debug('State abbreviations cannot have more than 2 characters);
}
if(stateAbbreviation.replaceAll('[^a-z]','').length()!=0){
    System.debug('State abbreviations cannot have lowercase characters');
}
if(stateAbbreviation.replaceAll('[^A-Za-z]','').length()!=0){
    System.debug('State abbreviations cannot have characters different from letters');
}
```

9) Type a code to create a simple calculator which does addition, subtraction, multiplication, and division with any 2 number
   a) When a user entered 10.2 and 5 and + sign your code should print "The result is 15.2" on the console
   b) When a user entered 10 and 5 and - sign your code should print "The result is 5.0" on the console
   c) When a user entered 10 and 5.3 and * sign your code should print "The result is 53.0" on the console
   d) When a user entered 10 and -5 and / signs your code should print "The result is -2.0" on the console

   SOLUTION

```
Double a = 10.2;
Double b = 5;
String operator = '+';
if(operator.equals('+')){
    System.debug(a+b);
}else if(operator.equals('-')){
    System.debug(a-b);
}else if(operator.equals('*')){
    System.debug(a*b);
}else if(operator.equals('/')){
    System.debug(a/b);
}
```

10) Type a code to print the messages about the Body Mass Index(BMI) for the given BMI values

Invalid BMI value < 0
Underweight = <18.5
Normal weight = 18.5 – 24.9
Overweight = 25 – 29.9
Obesity = BMI of 30 or greater

SOLUTION

```
Double bmi = 12;
if(bmi<0){
    System.debug('Invalid BMI value');
}else if(bmi<18.5){
    System.debug('Underweight');
}else if(bmi<24.9 && bmi>=18.5){
    System.debug('Normal weight');
}else if(bmi<29.9 && bmi>=25){
    System.debug('Overweight');
}else if(bmi>30){
    System.debug('Obesity');
}
```

1) Use ternary to print "Valid Password" if the password has at least 8 characters different from space characters. "Invalid Password" if the password has less than 8 characters different from the space character

SOLUTION

```
String password = 'a1b 2c3';
String isValid = password.deleteWhiteSpace().length()>7 ? 'Valid Password' : 'Invalid Password'; System.debug(isValid);
```

2) Use ternary to print
   a) "Isosceles Triangle" if two sides of a triangle are equal in length.
   b) "Equilateral Triangle" if all sides of a triangle are equal in length.
   c) "Neither isosceles nor equilateral" if a and b conditions are not satisfied

SOLUTION

```
Integer a = 5;
Integer b = 5;
Integer c = 5;
String typeOfTriangle = a==b && b==c ? 'Equilateral Triangle' : (a==b && b!=c || a==c && b!=c || b==c && a!=c ? 'Isosceles Triangle' : 'Neither isosceles, nor equilateral');
System.debug(typeOfTriangle);
```

3) Use ternary to print
   a) "Roundup by the last digit" and print the rounded value if the last digit of an integer is greater than or equal to 5
   b) "Round down by the last digit" and print the rounded value if the last digit of an integer is less than 5

Example
127 will be rounded up and the value will be 130
125 will be rounded up and the value will be 130
123 will be rounded down and the value will be 120

SOLUTION

```
Integer i = 125;
String result = Math.mod(i, 10)>=5 ? ('Round up by last digit:' + (i/10+1)*10) : ('Round down by  last digit:' + (i/10)*10);
System.debug(result);
```

4) Type Apex code by using nested ternary.
   Write a program to check if a year is a leap year or not.
   If the year is divisible by 100 then it must be divisible by 400.
   If a year is not divisible by 100 then it must be divisible by 4.

   SOLUTION

```
Integer y = 2021;
String isLeap = (Math.mod(y, 100)==0) ? ( (Math.mod(y,400)==0) ? ('Leap') : ('Not Leap') )
: ( (Math.mod(y, 4)==0) ? ('Leap') : ('Not Leap') );
System.debug(isLeap);
```

5) Type a code to check the password
   If it has more than 8 characters, the initial should be 'i'
   If it does not have more than 8 characters initial should be 'K'
   Solve the task by using nested-ternary

   SOLUTION

```
String p = 'XXXXXXXXX';
String isValid = (p.length()>8) ? ( (p.startsWith('i')) ? ('Valid') : ('Invalid') ) : (
(p.startsWith('K')) ? ('Valid') : ('Invalid') );
System.debug(isValid);
```

6) Type a code to calculate the absolute value of a number
   For positive numbers and zero absolute value is the same with the number
   For negative numbers to find absolute value multiply the number by -1

   SOLUTION

```
Integer i = 0;
Integer result = i<0 ? -1*i : i;
System.debug(result);
```

7) Write a program to print the minimum of 2 integers on the console by using ternary.

   SOLUTION

```
Integer i = 13;
Integer k = 13;
Integer result = i<k ? i : k;
System.debug(result);
```

8) If the number has 3 digits, the output will be "This number has 3 digits." Otherwise, the output will be "This number has no 3 digits."

SOLUTION

```
Integer i = -750;
String result = (i>99 && i<1000) || (i>-1000 && i<-99) ? 'This number has 3 digits' : 'This number has no 3 digits';
System.debug(result);
```

9) Print 'Even' for even integers, print 'Odd' for odd integers by using ternary.

SOLUTION

```
Integer i = 13;
String result = Math.mod(i, 2)==0 ? 'Even' : 'Odd';
System.debug(result);
```

10) If the number is positive print 'Positive', otherwise print 'Not positive' on the console by using ternary.

SOLUTION

```
Integer i = 12;
String result = i>0 ? 'Positive' : 'Not positive';
System.debug(result);
```

SWITCH-ON STATEMENT

1) Use switch statement to print
   a) "Winter" for December, January, February
   b) "Spring" for March, April, May
   c) "Summer" for June, July, August
   d) "Fall" for September, October, November
   e) "Invalid month name" for all the others

   SOLUTION

```
String monthName = 'XXX';
monthName = monthName.toLowerCase();
switch on monthName{
when 'december', 'january', 'february'{
    System.debug('Winter');
}
when 'march', 'april', 'may'{
    System.debug('Spring');
}
when 'june', 'july', 'august'{
    System.debug('Summer');
}
when 'september', 'october', 'november'{
    System.debug('Summer');
}
when else{
    System.debug('Invalid month name');
}
}
```

2) Print "Boy" if the gender is "Male" *(Ignore cases)*
   Print "Girl" if the gender is "Female" *(Ignore cases)*
   Print "Undefined" if the gender is different from "Male" and "Female"

   SOLUTION

```
String gender = 'FeMaLe';
switch on gender.toLowerCase(){
    when 'male'{
        System.debug('Boy');
    }
    when 'female'{
        System.debug('Girl');
    }
    when else{
        System.debug('Undefined');
    }
}
```

3) Use a switch statement to print the name of the month when you enter the number of the month. For example; if the user enters 1 your code should print "January", if the user enters 2 your code should print "February" etc. if the user enters an invalid month number your code should print "Invalid number"

SOLUTION

```
Integer numOfMonth = 3;
switch on numOfMonth{
when 1{
    System.debug('January');
}
when 2{
    System.debug('February');
}
when 3{
    System.debug('March');
}
when 4{
    System.debug('April');
}
when 5{
    System.debug('May');
}
when 6{
    System.debug('June');
}
when 7{
    System.debug('July');
}
when 8{
    System.debug('August');
}
when 9{
    System.debug('September');
}
when 10{
    System.debug('October');
}
when 11{
    System.debug('November');
}
when 12{
    System.debug('December');
}
when else{
    System.debug('Invalid number');
}
}
```

4) Create a function to check the grammatical rules for full names then use the function in the switch statement. (Difficult Challenge)
   a) Your code should print 'Error in initials' for 'ali Can', 'Ali can', 'ali can'
   b) Your code should print 'First name or last name missed' for single words like 'Ali' or 'Can' or 'ali'
   c) Your code should print 'Format error' for all uppercases like 'ALI CAN'
   d) Your code should print 'Name was not entered' for empty String like '' and one or more space characters like ' ' or ' '
   e) Your code should print 'Invalid Name' if the name has any character different from letters.

   Note 1: If the abbreviation has more than 1 error all related error messages should be printed. For example; for "ali3" your code should print "Error in initials", "First name or last name missed", and "Invalid Name"

   Note 2: As you can see in the following solution, you should use boolean in conditions, and "boolean" cannot be used in a switch statement, therefore you cannot solve that question by using a switch statement

SOLUTION

```
String fullName = 'ali Can?';
String initialOfFirst = fullName.substring(0,1);

Integer indexOfSpace = fullName.trim().indexOf(' ');
String initialOfLast = fullName.substring(indexOfSpace+1,indexOfSpace+2);

Boolean isFirstUpper = (initialOfFirst.charAt(0)>=65 &&  initialOfFirst.charAt(0)<=90);
Boolean isLastUpper = (initialOfLast.charAt(0)>=65 &&  initialOfLast.charAt(0)<=90);
if(indexOfSpace==-1){
    System.debug('First name or last name missed');
}
if(!isFirstUpper || !isLastUpper){
    System.debug('Error in initials');
}
if(fullName.equals(fullName.toUpperCase())){
    System.debug('Format error');
}
if(fullName.deleteWhiteSpace().length()==0){
    System.debug('Name was not entered');
}
if(fullName.deleteWhiteSpace().replaceAll('[A-Za-z]','').length()>0){
    System.debug('Invalid Name');
}
```

5) Create a function to check the format of state abbreviations in the USA then use the function in the switch statement. (Difficult Challenge)
a) Your code should print "State abbreviations cannot have more than 2 characters" if the abbreviation has more than 2 characters
b) Your code should print "State abbreviations cannot have lowercase characters" if the abbreviation has lowercase characters
c) Your code should print "State abbreviations cannot have characters different from letters" if the abbreviation has characters different from letters.
Note 1: If the abbreviation has more than 1 error all related error messages should be printed. For example; for "fl3" your code should print, "State abbreviations cannot have more than 2 characters", "State abbreviations cannot have lowercase characters", and "State abbreviations cannot have characters different from letters"
Note 2: As you can see in the following solution, you should use boolean in conditions, and "boolean" cannot be used in a switch statement, therefore you cannot solve that question by using a switch statement

SOLUTION

```
String stateAbbreviation = 'Fl3';
if(stateAbbreviation.length()>2){
    System.debug('State abbreviations cannot have more than 2 characters);
}
if(stateAbbreviation.replaceAll('[^a-z]','').length()!=0){
    System.debug('State abbreviations cannot have lowercase characters');
}
if(stateAbbreviation.replaceAll('[A-Za-z]','').length()!=0){
    System.debug('State abbreviations cannot have characters different from letters');
}
```

6) Use a switch statement to create a simple calculator which does addition, subtraction, multiplication, and division with any 2 numbers
   a) When a user entered 10.2 and 5 and + sign your code should print "The result is 15.2" on the console
   b) When a user entered 10 and 5 and - sign your code should print "The result is 5.0" on the console
   c) When a user entered 10 and 5.3 and * sign your code should print "The result is 53.0" on the console
   d) When a user entered 10 and -5 and / signs your code should print "The result is -2.0" on the console
   e) When a user entered 10 and -5 and an operation different from +, -, *, / your code should print "That operation cannot be done"

SOLUTION

```
Double a = 10.2;
Double b = 5;
String operator = '+';
switch on operator{
when '+'{
    System.debug(a+b);
}
when '-'{
    System.debug(a-b);
}
when '*'{
    System.debug(a*b);
}
when '/'{
    System.debug(a/b);
}
when else{
    System.debug('That operation cannot be done');
}
}
```

7) Use a switch statement to create a converter that converts mile to km, second to hour, fahrenheit to celsius. Find the formulas for conversions from Google.
   a) When a user entered 10 and mileToKm String, your code should print "16 km" (The number will be dynamic) on the console
   b) When a user entered 7200 and secondsToHours String, your code should print "2 Hours"(The number will be dynamic) on the console
   c) When user entered 83 and fahrenheitToCelsius String, your code should print "28.3333 celsius"(The number will be dynamic) on the console
   d) When user entered operation different from mileToKm, secondsToHours, fahrenheitToCelsius your code should print "That operation was not defined for that converter"

SOLUTION

```
Double mile = 10;
Double seconds = 7200;
Double fahrenheit = 83;
String operator = 'fahrenheitToCelsius';
switch on operator{
when 'mileToKm'{
    System.debug(mile*1.60934);
}
when 'secondsToHours'{
    System.debug((seconds/60)/60);
}
when 'fahrenheitToCelsius'{
    System.debug((fahrenheit-32)*5/9 );
}
when else{
    System.debug('That operation was not defined for that converter');
    }
}
```

8) Create an Enum and put the browser names in it like CHROME, SAFARI, IE, FIREFOX, YANDEX. Use switch statement and print 'I am using CHROME' for CHROME, 'I am using SAFARI' for SAFARI, 'I am using IE for IE', 'I am using FIREFOX for FIREFOX', and 'I am using YANDEX' for YANDEX, 'Not valid browser' for browsers different from CHROME, SAFARI, IE, FIREFOX, YANDEX.

Note: You should create an enum on the developer console

SOLUTION

```
public enum Browsers{
 CHROME, SAFARI, IE, FIREFOX, YANDEX
}
String browser = Browsers.CHROME;
switch on browser{
when 'CHROME'{
    System.debug('I am using CHROME');
}
when 'SAFARI'{
System.debug('I am using SAFARI');
}
when 'IE'{
    System.debug('I am using IE for IE');
}
when 'FIREFOX'{
    System.debug('I am using FIREFOX for FIREFOX');
}
when 'YANDEX'{
    System.debug('I am using YANDEX');
}
when else{
    System.debug('Not valid browser');
}
}
```

9) Create an Enum whose name is 'Seasons' and print the following by using the Enum in the switch-on statement
For winter print 'Snowboarding'
For summer and spring print 'Fishing'
For fall print 'Trekking'

SOLUTION

```apex
public enum Seasons {
    WINTER, SUMMER, FALL, SPRING
}

switch on Seasons.SUMMER{
    when WINTER{
    System.debug('Snowboarding');
    }
    when SUMMER, SPRING{
    System.debug('Fishing');
    }
    when FALL{
    System.debug('Trekking');
    }
    when else{
    System.debug('Undefined');
    }
}
```

10) Create a method that gives you a random alphabetical character in Apex01 Class then print the following by using the method.
Print "First Character" for 'A' and 'a'
Print "Second Character" for 'B' and 'b'
Print "Third Character" for 'C' and 'c'
Print "Forth Character" for 'D' and 'd'
Print "Other Characters" for all others

SOLUTION

```apex
public class Batch04Apex01 {
    public static String getRandomAlphabet(){
        String alphabets = 'ABCDEFGHIJKLMNOPQRSTUVWXYZabcdefghijklmnopqrstuvwxyz';
        Integer maxIndex = alphabets.length()-1;
        Integer randomIndex = Integer.valueOf(Math.random()*maxIndex);
        //Math.random()*maxIndex will return random values from 0 to maxIndex
        return alphabets.substring(randomIndex, randomIndex+1);
    }
}

switch on Apex01.getRandomAlphabet(){
    when 'A', 'a'{
        System.debug('First Character');
    }
    when 'B', 'b'{
        System.debug('Second Character');
    }
    when 'C', 'c'{
        System.debug('Third Character');
    }
    when 'D', 'd'{
        System.debug('Fourth Character');
    }
    when else{
        System.debug('Other Characters');
    }
}
```

LOOPS

1) Type all integers which are divisible by 4 and divisible by 6 from 120 to 11 in the same line with a space between two consecutive integers

SOLUTION

1. Way:
```
String s = '';
for(Integer i=120; i>10; i--){
if(Math.mod(i,4)==0 && Math.mod(i,6)==0){
s = s + i + ' ';
}
}
System.debug(s);
```

2. Way:
```
String s = '';
Integer i=120;
while(i>10){
if(Math.mod(i,4)==0 && Math.mod(i,6)==0){
s = s + i + ' ';
}
i--;
}
System.debug(s);
```

3. Way:
```
String s = '';
Integer i=120;
do{
if(Math.mod(i,4)==0 && Math.mod(i,6)==0){
s = s + i + ' ';
}
i--;
}while(i>10);
System.debug(s);
```

2) Type a code to print repeated characters in a String. For example; accessories ⇒ ces

SOLUTION

1. Way:

```
String s = 'accessories';
String d = '';
for(Integer i=0; i<s.length(); i++){
String c = s.substring(i,i+1);
if(s.indexOf(c)!=s.lastIndexOf(c)){
if(!d.contains(c)){
d = d + c;
}
}
}
System.debug(d);
```

2. Way:

```
String s = 'accessories';
String d = '';
Integer i=0;
while(i<s.length()){
String c = s.substring(i,i+1);
if(s.indexOf(c)!=s.lastIndexOf(c)){
if(!d.contains(c)){
d = d + c;
}
}
i++;
}
System.debug(d);
```

3. Way:

```
String s = 'accessories';
String d = '';
Integer i=0;
Do{
String c = s.substring(i,i+1);
if(s.indexOf(c)!=s.lastIndexOf(c)){
if(!d.contains(c)){
d = d + c;
}
}
i++;
}while(i<s.length());
System.debug(d);
```

3) Type a code to check whether a String is a palindrome or not. If a String is the same as its reverse then it is called a palindrome. For example; "anna", "123321" are palindromes

SOLUTION

1. Way:
```
String s = 'runnur';
String r = '';
for(Integer i=s.length()-1; i>-1; i--){
        String c = s.substring(i,i+1);
r = r + c;
}
if(s.equals(r)){
System.debug(s + ' is palindrome');
}else{
System.debug(s + ' is not palindrome');
}
```

2. Way:
```
String s = 'runnur';
String r = '';
Integer i=s.length()-1;
while(i>-1){
String c = s.substring(i,i+1);
r = r + c;
i--;
}
if(s.equals(r)){
System.debug(s + ' is palindrome');
}else{
System.debug(s + ' is not palindrome');
}
```

3. Way:
```
String s = 'runnur';
String r = '';
Integer i=s.length()-1;
do{
String c = s.substring(i,i+1);
r = r + c;
i--;
}while(i>-1);
if(s.equals(r)){
System.debug(s + ' is palindrome');
}else{
System.debug(s + ' is not palindrome');
}
```

4) Type a code to print the unique digits in an integer. Example; 223878 ⇒ 37

SOLUTION

1. Way:
```
Integer num = 223878;
String s = String.valueOf(num);
String d = '';
for(Integer i=0; i<s.length(); i++){
String c = s.substring(i,i+1);
if(s.indexOf(c)==s.lastIndexOf(c)){
d = d + c;
}
}
System.debug(d);
```

2. Way:
```
Integer num = 223878;
String s = String.valueOf(num);
String d = '';
Integer i = 0;
while(i<s.length()){
String c = s.substring(i,i+1);
if(s.indexOf(c)==s.lastIndexOf(c)){
d = d + c;
}
i++;
}
System.debug(d);
```

3. Way:
```
Integer num = 223878;
String s = String.valueOf(num);
String d = '';
Integer i = 0;
do{
String c = s.substring(i,i+1);
if(s.indexOf(c)==s.lastIndexOf(c)){
d = d + c;
}
i++;
}while(i<s.length());
System.debug(d);
```

5) Type a code to draw the following image by using a for loop.
A A A A A
A A A A A
A A A A A

SOLUTION

1. Way:
```
Integer rows = 3;
Integer columns = 5;
for(Integer i=1; i<=rows; i++){
String s = '';
for(Integer k=1; k<=columns; k++){
s = s + 'A ';
}
System.debug(s);
}
```

2. Way:
```
Integer rows = 3;
Integer columns = 5;
Integer i=1;
while(i<=rows){
String s = '';
for(Integer k=1; k<=columns; k++){
s = s + 'A ';
}
System.debug(s);
i++;
}
```

3. Way:
```
Integer rows = 3;
Integer columns = 5;
Integer i=1;
do{
String s = '';
for(Integer k=1; k<=columns; k++){
s = s + 'A ';
}
System.debug(s);
i++;
}while(i<=rows);
```

6) Type a code to draw the following image by using a for loop.

A
A A
A A A
A A A A

SOLUTION

1. Way:
```
Integer rows = 4;
for(Integer i=1; i<=rows; i++){
String s = '';
for(Integer k=1; k<=i; k++){
s = s + 'A ';
}
System.debug(s);
}
```

2. Way:
```
Integer rows = 4;
Integer i=1;
while(i<=rows){
String s = '';
for(Integer k=1; k<=i; k++){
s = s + 'A ';
}
System.debug(s);
i++;
}
```

3. Way:
```
Integer rows = 4;
Integer i=1;
do{
String s = '';
for(Integer k=1; k<=i; k++){
s = s + 'A ';
}
System.debug(s);
i++;
}while(i<=rows);
```

7) Type a code to create multiplication table like
   3x1=3 3x2=6 3x3=9 3x4=12 3x5=15 3x6=18 3x7=21 3x8=24 3x9=27 3x10=30

SOLUTION

1. Way:
```
Integer num = 3;
for(Integer i=1; i<11; i++){
System.debug(num + 'x' + i +'=' + num*i);
}
```

2. Way:
```
Integer num = 3;
Integer i=1;
while(i<11){
System.debug(num + 'x' + i +'=' + num*i);
i++;
}
```

3. Way:
```
Integer num = 3;
Integer i=1;
do{
System.debug(num + 'x' + i +'=' + num*i);
i++;
}while(i<11);
```

8) Type a code to print odd integers from 20 to 3 in the same line with a space between two consecutive ones.

SOLUTION

```
String s = '';
for(Integer i=20; i>2; i--){
   if(Math.mod(i, 2)!=0){
      s = s + i + ' ';
   }
}
System.debug(s);
```

9) Type a code to print all lowercase characters in a String with an asterisk.
For example; 'Ali Can?' ==> l*i*a*n*

SOLUTION

1. Way:
```
String s = 'Ali Can?';
s = s.replaceAll('[^a-z]', '');
String t = '';
for(Integer i=0; i<s.length(); i++){
String r = s.substring(i,i+1);
t = t + r + '*';
}
System.debug(t);
```

2. Way:
```
String s = 'Ali Can?';
s = s.replaceAll('[^a-z]', '');
String t = '';
Integer i=0;
while(i<s.length()){
String r = s.substring(i,i+1);
t = t + r + '*';
i++;
}
System.debug(t);
```

3. Way:
```
String s = 'Ali Can?';
s = s.replaceAll('[^a-z]', '');
String t = '';
Integer i=0;
do{
String r = s.substring(i,i+1);
t = t + r + '*';
i++;
}while(i<s.length());
System.debug(t);
```

10) Type a code to draw the following image by using a for loop.

```
A A A A A A A A
A X X X X X X A
A X X X X X X A
A X X X X X X A
```

SOLUTION

1. Way:
```
Integer rows = 4;
Integer columns = 8;
for(Integer i=1; i<=rows; i++){
String s = '';
if(i==1 || i==rows){
for(Integer k=1; k<=columns; k++){
s = s + 'A ';
}
System.debug(s);
}else{
s = s + 'A ';
for(Integer m=2; m<columns; m++){
s = s + 'X ';
}
s = s + 'A ';
System.debug(s);
}
}
```

2. Way:
```
Integer rows = 4;
Integer columns = 8;
Integer i=1;
while(i<=rows){
String s = '';
if(i==1 || i==rows){
for(Integer k=1; k<=columns; k++){
s = s + 'A ';
}
System.debug(s);
}else{
s = s + 'A ';
for(Integer m=2; m<columns; m++){
s = s + 'X ';
}
s = s + 'A ';
System.debug(s);
}
i++;
}
```

3. Way:

```
Integer rows = 4;
Integer columns = 8;
Integer i=1;
do{
String s = '';
if(i==1 || i==rows){
for(Integer k=1; k<=columns; k++){
s = s + 'A ';
}
System.debug(s);
}else{
s = s + 'A ';
for(Integer m=2; m<columns; m++){
s = s + 'X ';
}
s = s + 'A ';
System.debug(s);
}
i++;
}while(i<=rows);
```

11) Type a code to reverse a String. For example; Ali ==> ilA

SOLUTION

```
String t = 'Ali';
String rev = '';
for(Integer i=t.length()-1; i>-1; i--){
    rev = rev + t.substring(i,i+1);
}
System.debug(rev);
```

12) Type a code to find the sum of the integers from 3 to 14

SOLUTION

```
Integer sum = 0;
for(Integer i=3; i<15; i++){
    sum = sum+i;
}
System.debug(sum);
```

13) Type a code to print digits just in the decimal part of the given decimal number with an asterisk. For example; 75.4238 ⇒ *4*2*3*8

SOLUTION

1. Way:

```
Double num = 75.4238;
String s = String.valueOf(num);
Integer idxOfComma = s.indexOf('.');
String decimalPart = s.substring(idxOfComma + 1);
String t = '';
for(Integer i=0; i<decimalPart.length(); i++){
String r = decimalPart.substring(i,i+1);
t = t + '*' + r;
}
System.debug(t);
```

2. Way:

```
Double num = 75.4238;
String s = String.valueOf(num);
Integer idxOfComma = s.indexOf('.');
String decimalPart = s.substring(idxOfComma + 1);
String t = '';
Integer i=0;
while(i<decimalPart.length()){
String r = decimalPart.substring(i,i+1);
t = t + '*' + r;
i++;
}
System.debug(t);
```

3. Way:

```
Double num = 75.4238;
String s = String.valueOf(num);
Integer idxOfComma = s.indexOf('.');
String decimalPart = s.substring(idxOfComma + 1);
String t = '';
Integer i=0;
do{
String r = decimalPart.substring(i,i+1);
t = t + '*' + r;
i++;
}while(i<decimalPart.length());
System.debug(t);
```

14) Type a code to find the multiplication of the integers from 3 to 9

SOLUTION

```
Integer m = 1;
for(Integer i=3; i<10; i++){
    m = m*i;
}
System.debug(m);
```

15) Type a code to print characters from 'C' to 'A' on the console by using the do-while loop

SOLUTION

```
Integer asciiValue = 'C'.charAt(0);
String result = '';

do{
    result = result + String.fromCharArray(new List<Integer>{asciiValue});
    asciiValue--;
}while(asciiValue>='A'.charAt(0));
    System.debug(result);
```

16) Type all characters before the first occurrence of 'm' in a String

SOLUTION

```
String s = 'Christmas';
String result = '';

for(Integer i=0; i<s.length(); i++){
    String c = s.substring(i,i+1);
    if(c.equals('m')){
        break;
    }
    result = result + c;
}
System.debug(result);
```

17) Type a code to find the sum of the digits in an integer

SOLUTION

1. Way:
```
Integer num = 753;
Integer sumOfDigits = 0;
while(num>0){
   sumOfDigits = sumOfDigits + Math.mod(num, 10);
   num = num/10;
}
System.debug(sumOfDigits);
```

2. Way:
```
Integer n = 753;
Integer sumOfDigits = 0;

for(Integer i = n; i>0; i=i/10){
   sumOfDigits = sumOfDigits + Math.mod(i, 10);
}
System.debug(sumOfDigits);
```

18) Type a code to draw the following image by using a for loop.
```
* * * * * *
* * * * *
* * * *
* * *
* *
*
```

SOLUTION

```
Integer term=6;
String s = '';

for(Integer i=1; i<=term; i++){
   for(Integer k=term; k>=i; k--){
      s = s + '* ';
   }
   System.debug(s);
   s = '';
}
```

19) Type a code to print unique characters in a String. For example; Hello ==> Heo

1. Way:
```
String s = 'Hello';
Integer i = 0;
while(i<s.length()){
    String c = s.substring(i,i+1);
    if(s.indexOf(c) == s.lastIndexOf(c)){
        System.debug(c);
    }
    i++;
}
```

2. Way:
```
String s = 'Hello';
Integer k = 0;
while(k<s.length()){
    String d = s.substring(k, k+1);
    if(s.countMatches(d)==1){
        System.debug(d);
    }
    k++;
}
```

20) Type a code to find the sum of the unique digits of an integer

Example
$12133455 \Rightarrow 2+4=6$

```
Integer p = 12133455;
String r = String.valueOf(p);
Integer sumOfUniqueDigits = 0;

for(Integer i=0; i<r.length(); i++){
    String c = r.substring(i,i+1);
    if(r.countMatches(c)==1){
        sumOfUniqueDigits = sumOfUniqueDigits + Integer.valueOf(c);
    }
}
System.debug(sumOfUniqueDigits);
```

21) Type a code to print integers from 3 to 10 except 5

SOLUTION

```
for(Integer i=3; i<11; i++){
    if(i==5){
        continue;
    }
    System.debug(i);
}
```

22) Find the total number of characters different from space and punctuation marks in a String

SOLUTION

```
String s = 'Apex is a strongly typed, object-oriented programming language.';
s = s.deleteWhiteSpace().replaceAll('\\p{Punct}', '');
System.debug(s.length());
```

ARRAYS

1) Find the middle element in an integer array

   ### Example
   (12, 5, 8) ==> (5, 8, 12) ==> Output=8
   (12, 5, 8, 13) ==> (5, 8, 12, 13) ==> Output=(8+12)/2 = 10

   SOLUTION

```
Integer[] a = new Integer[]{12, 5, 8, 13};
a.sort();

if(Math.mod(a.size(),2)!=0){
    Integer indexOfMiddleElement = a.size()/2;
    System.debug(a[indexOfMiddleElement]);
}else{
    Integer indexOfMiddleElement = a.size()/2;
    Integer averageValue = (a[indexOfMiddleElement] + a[indexOfMiddleElement-1])/2;
    System.debug(averageValue);
}
```

2) Find the smallest positive element and greatest negative element in an integer array

   ### Example
   (-12, 18, -5, 23, -2) ==> Smallest positive is 18, greatest negative is -2 the sum is -2+18=16

   SOLUTION

```
Integer[] a = new Integer[]{-12, 18, -5, 23, -2};
a.sort();

Integer minPositive = a[a.size()-1];
Integer maxNegative = a[0];

for(Integer w : a){

    if(w>=0){
        minPositive = Math.min(minPositive, w);
    }
    if(w<0){
        maxNegative = Math.max(maxNegative, w);
    }
}
System.debug('Minimum positive: ' + minPositive);
System.debug('Maximum negative: ' + maxNegative);
```

3) Find the elements whose length is the smallest in a String array
Example
(Kemal, Jonathan, Mark, Angie) ==> Output is Mark

SOLUTION

```
String[] b = new String[]{'Kemal', 'Jonathan', 'Mark', 'Angie', 'Veli'};

Integer minLength = b[0].length();

for(String w : b){
    minLength = Math.min(minLength, w.length());
}
for(String w : b){
    if(minLength == w.length()){
        System.debug(w);
    }
}
```

4) Get the initials of the elements in a String array, if the String ends with 'n' or 'k'
Example
(Kemal, Jonathan, Mark, Jackson, Ali) ==> Output is JJM

SOLUTION

```
String[] c = new String[]{'Kemal', 'Jonathan', 'Mark', 'Jackson', 'Ali'};

String initials = '';

for(String w : c){
    if(w.endsWith('n') || w.endsWith('k')){
        initials = initials + w.substring(0,1);
    }
}
System.debug(initials);
```

5) Find the total number of characters used in String array elements

Example
(Kemal, Jonathan, Mark, Jackson, Ali) ==> Output is 27

SOLUTION

```
String[] d = new String[]{'Kemal', 'Jonathan', 'Mark', 'Jackson', 'Ali'};
Integer sum = 0;

for(String w : d){
   sum = sum + w.length();
}
System.debug('The sum is ' + sum);
```

6) Count how many words start with 'a' or 'A' in a given String

SOLUTION

```
String s = 'Apex is an object-oriented programming language';

String[] arr = s.split(' ');
Integer counter = 0;

for(String w : arr){
   if(w.startsWith('a') || w.startsWith('A')){
      counter++;
   }
}
System.debug('The number of words which starts with a or A is : ' + counter);
```

7) Find the number of vowels in a String

SOLUTION

```apex
String s = 'Apex is an object oriented programming language';

String[] arr = s.toLowerCase().split('');
Integer counter = 0;

for(String w : arr){
   switch on w{
      when 'a', 'e', 'i', 'o', 'u'{
         counter++;
      }
   }
}
System.debug('The number of vowels: ' + counter);
```

8) Type a code to find if a given element exists in a given array

SOLUTION

```apex
String[] arr = new String[]{'Apex', 'is', 'an', 'object', 'oriented', 'programming', 'language'};

String s = 'object';
Integer counter = 0;

for(String w : arr){
   if(w.equalsIgnoreCase(s)){
      counter++;
   }
}

if(counter>0){
   System.debug(s + ' exists');
}else{
   System.debug(s + ' does not exist');
}
```

9) Type a code to find array elements whose first and last characters are the same

SOLUTION

```
String[] arr = new String[]{'alabama', 'pick', 'sas', 'sets', 'pex'};
Integer size = arr.size();

for(Integer i=0; i<size; i++){
    String firstChar = arr[i].substring(0, 1);
    String lastChar = arr[i].substring(arr[i].length()-1);

    if(firstChar.equals(lastChar)){
        System.debug(arr[i]);
    }
}
```

10) Type a code to find sum of the number of characters of array elements

SOLUTION

```
String[] arr = new String[]{'alabama', 'pick', 'sas', 'sets', 'pex'};
Integer sum = 0;

for(String w : arr){
    sum = sum + w.length();
}
System.debug(sum);
```

11) Type a code to put all zeros to end in an integer array.

Example
(5, 0, 2, 0, 3) ==> (5, 2, 3, 0, 0, 3)

SOLUTION

```
Integer[] arr = new Integer[]{5, 0, 2, 0};

Integer[] brr = new Integer[arr.size()];

Integer firstIdx = 0;
Integer lastIdx = arr.size()-1;

for(Integer i=0; i<arr.size(); i++){
    if(arr[i]!=0){
        brr[firstIdx] = arr[i];
        firstIdx++;
    }else{
        brr[lastIdx]=0;
        lastIdx--;
    }
}
System.debug(brr);
```

LISTS

1) Find the sum of all list elements in an integer list

SOLUTION

```
List<Integer> myList = new List<Integer>{12, 31, 7, 13, 10};
Integer sum = 0;
for(Integer w : myList){
    sum = sum + w;
}
System.debug(sum);
```

2) Find the multiplication of all even list elements in an integer list

SOLUTION

1. Way:
```
List<Integer> myList = new List<Integer>{12, 31, 7, 13, 10};
Integer mult = 1;
for(Integer w : myList){
    if(Math.mod(w,2)!=0){
        continue;
    }
    mult = mult * w;
}
System.debug(mult);
```

2. Way:
```
List<Integer> myList = new List<Integer>{12, 31, 7, 13, 10};
Integer mult = 1;
for(Integer w : myList){
    if(Math.mod(w,2)==0){
        mult = mult * w;
    }
}
System.debug(mult);
```

3) Find the sum of all list elements before the first occurrence of 13 in an integer list

SOLUTION

```
List<Integer> myList = new List<Integer>{12, 31, 7, 13, 10};
Integer sum = 0;
for(Integer w : myList){
    if(w==13){
        break;
    }
    sum = sum + w;
}
System.debug(sum);
```

4) Check if elements are in descending order in a list

Example
(Yellow, Blue, Red, Green) ==> Output: It is not in descending order
(Yellow, Red, Green, Blue) ==> Output: It is in descending order

SOLUTION

```
List<String> e = new List<String>{ 'Yellow', 'Red', 'Green', 'Blue'};

List<String> f = new List<String>(e);
f.sort();

Integer size = e.size();
Integer flag = 0;

for(Integer i=0; i<size; i++){
    if(f.get(i).equals(e.get(size-1-i))){
        flag++;
    }
}
if(flag == size){
    System.debug('It is in descending order');
}else{
    System.debug('It is not in descending order');
}
```

5) If the list has 15 as element, change all 15s to 51

Example
(12, 11, 15, 34, 43) ==> Output is (12, 11, 51, 34, 43)

SOLUTION

```
List<Integer> g = new List<Integer>{12, 11, 15, 34, 15, 43};

if(g.contains(15)){
    for(Integer w : g){
        if(w==15){
            Integer idx = g.indexOf(15);
                g.set(idx, 51);
        }
    }
    System.debug(g);
}else{
    System.debug('There is no expected element');
}
```

6) Increase the value of every element except 7 and 10 by 2 in a List

Example
(12, 31, 7, 13, 10) ==> Output is (14, 33, 7, 15, 10)

SOLUTION

```
List<Integer> h = new List<Integer>{12, 31, 7, 13, 10};

for(Integer w : h){
    if(w==7 || w==10){
        continue;
    }
    h.set(h.indexOf(w), w+2);
}
System.debug(h);
```

7) If a list has 15 or 13, remove them. Multiple 15 and multiple 13 are out of scope.

Example
(10, 31, 15, 13, 54) ==> Output is (10, 31, 54)

SOLUTION

```
if(!h.contains(15) && !h.contains(13)){
    System.debug('The list does not contain 13 and 15');
}else {
        if(h.contains(15)){
                Integer idx15 = h.indexOf(15);
                h.remove(idx15);
        }

        if(h.contains(13)){
                Integer idx13 = h.indexOf(13);
                h.remove(idx13);
        }
        System.debug(h);
}
```

8) Find the closest 2 integers in an Integer List

Example
(12, 31, 15, 13, 54) ==> Output is 12 and 13

SOLUTION

```
List<Integer> h = new List<Integer>{12, 31, 15, 13, 54};
h.sort();
Integer minDiff = h[1] - h[0];

for(Integer i=1; i<h.size(); i++){
    minDiff = Math.min(minDiff, h.get(i)-h.get(i-1));
}

for(Integer i=1; i<h.size(); i++){
    if(h.get(i)-h.get(i-1) == minDiff){
        System.debug(h.get(i) + ' and ' + h.get(i-1));
    }
}
```

9) Check if all elements are unique in an integer List by using loops.

```
List<Integer> myList = new List<Integer>();
myList.add(12);
myList.add(84);
myList.add(12);
myList.add(132);

Integer counter = 0;
for(Integer w : myList){
    for(Integer k : myList){
      if(w==k){
         counter++;
      }
    }
}
if(counter==myList.size()){
    System.debug('There is no any repeated element');
}else{
    System.debug('At least one element was repeated');
}
```

10) Find the sum of all prices given in a String list

Example
```
List<String> myList = new List<String>{'$12.99', '$23.60', '$8.25', '$54.45'}; ==> 99.29
```

```
List<String> myList = new List<String>{'$12.99', '$23.60', '$8.25', '$54.45'};
Decimal sum = 0;

for(String w : myList){
      Decimal price = Decimal.valueOf(w.remove('$'));
    sum = sum + price;
}
System.debug(sum);
```

11) Find the sum of the least and the greatest price given in a String list

Example
List<String> myList = new List<String>{'$12.99', '$8.25', '$23.60', '$54.45'}; ==> 62.70

SOLUTION

```
List<String> myList = new List<String>{'$12.99', '$23.60', '$8.25', '$54.45'};
List<Decimal> decimalList = new List<Decimal>();

for(String w : myList){
        Decimal price = Decimal.valueOf(w.remove('$'));
    decimalList.add(price);
}
decimalList.sort();
Decimal sum = decimalList.get(0) + decimalList.get(decimalList.size()-1);
System.debug(sum);
```

SETS

1) Type the code that shows how many different elements there are in a list.

   Example
   List<Integer> myList = new List<Integer>{12, 13, 7, 13, 7, 7}; ==> 3

   SOLUTION

   List<Integer> myList = new List<Integer>{12, 13, 7, 13, 7, 7};

   Set<Integer> mySet = new Set<Integer>(myList);
   System.debug(mySet.size());

2) Type a code to print different characters used in a String

   Example
   'Mississippi' ⇒ Misp

   SOLUTION

   String s = 'Mississippi';

   String[] arr = s.split('');
   System.debug(arr);

   Set<String> mySet = new Set<String>(arr);
   System.debug(mySet);

3) Type a code to print the common elements between a Set and a List

   SOLUTION

   List<Integer> myList = new List<Integer>{12, 7, 13, 7, 7, 13, 13, 5};

   Set<Integer> mySet = new Set<Integer>();
   mySet.add(10);
   mySet.add(7);
   mySet.add(35);
   mySet.add(13);

   mySet.retainAll(myList);
   System.debug(mySet);

4) Type a code to print the different elements in a Set from a List

   SOLUTION

   List<Integer> myList = new List<Integer>{12, 7, 13, 7, 7, 13, 13, 5};

   Set<Integer> mySet = new Set<Integer>();
   mySet.add(10);
   mySet.add(7);
   mySet.add(35);
   mySet.add(13);

   mySet.removeAll(myList);
   System.debug(mySet);

5) Type a code to check if a List has repeated elements or not

   SOLUTION

   List<Integer> myList = new List<Integer>{12, 7, 13, 7, 7, 13, 13, 5};

   Set<Integer> mySet = new Set<Integer>(myList);

   if(myList.size()>mySet.size()){
   System.debug('The list has repeated elements');
   }else{
   System.debug('The list does not have repeated elements');
   }

MAPS

1) There is a Map that contains product names as keys and the number of the products as value. Type a code to find the total number of products.

SOLUTION

```
Map<String, Integer> product = new Map<String, Integer>();
product.put('Laptop', 12);
product.put('TV', 53);
product.put('Refrigerator', 12);
product.put('Music System', 87);

List<Integer> numOfProducts = product.values();

Integer sum = 0;
for(Integer w : numOfProducts){
    sum = sum + w;
}
System.debug(sum);
```

2) There is a Map that contains product names as key and the number of the products as value. Type a code to check if 'Laptop' is among the products.

SOLUTION

```
Map<String, Integer> product = new Map<String, Integer>();
product.put('Laptop', 12);
product.put('TV', 53);
product.put('Refrigerator', 12);
product.put('Music System', 87);

String expectedProduct = 'Laptop';
if(product.containsKey(expectedProduct)){
    System.debug(expectedProduct + ' exists');
}else{
    System.debug(expectedProduct + ' does not exist');
}
```

3) There is a Map that contains product names as key and the number of the products as value. Print the prices in ascending order.

SOLUTION

```
Map<String, Integer> product = new Map<String, Integer>();
product.put('Laptop', 12);
product.put('TV', 53);
product.put('Refrigerator', 12);
product.put('Music System', 87);

List<Integer> productPrices = product.values();
productPrices.sort();

System.debug(productPrices);
```

4) Type a code to count the number of occurrences of the words in a String. (Case insensitive)

SOLUTION

```
String s = 'Apex is easy. Type a codes to learn apex. To earn money learn apex.';
System.debug('Before removing punctuation marks: ' + s);

s = s.replaceAll('\\p{Punct}','').toLowerCase();
System.debug('After removing punctuation marks: ' + s);

Map<String, Integer> wordsOccurence = new Map<String, Integer>();

String[] words = s.split(' ');

for(String w : words){
    Integer numOfOccurence = wordsOccurence.get(w);
    if(numOfOccurence == null ){
        wordsOccurence.put(w, 1);
    }else{
        wordsOccurence.put(w, numOfOccurence+1);
    }
}
System.debug(wordsOccurence);
```

5) There is a Map that contains product names as key and the number of the products as value. Print the product names in alphabetical order.

SOLUTION

```
Map<String, Integer> product = new Map<String, Integer>();
product.put('Laptop', 12);
product.put('TV', 53);
product.put('Refrigerator', 12);
product.put('Music System', 87);

Set<String> productNamesAsSet = product.keySet();

List<String> productNamesAsList = new List<String>(productNamesAsSet);
productNamesAsList.sort();

System.debug(productNamesAsList);
```

6) How to check the number of repeated elements in a List

SOLUTION

```
List<Integer> myList = new List<Integer>{12, 21, 12, 13, 12, 21, 35};
Map<Integer, Integer> myMap = new Map<Integer, Integer>();

for(Integer w : myList){
    Integer numOfOccurence = myMap.get(w);
    if(numOfOccurence==null){
        myMap.put(w, 1);
    }else{
        myMap.put(w, numOfOccurence+1);
    }
}
List<Integer> myValues = myMap.values();
Integer counter = 0;

for(Integer w : myValues){
        if(w>1){
        counter++;
    }
}
System.debug('There are ' + counter + ' repeated elements');
```

ANSWER KEYS

Variables

1	2	3	4	5	6	7	8	9	10
A	A, B, C, D	A	A	B, C, D	A	A	A, B, C, D	C	C

String manipulations

1	2	3	4	5	6	7	8	9	10
A	B	A, B, D	A	A	B, C	B, D	D	C, D	A, D

11	12	13	14	15	16	17	18
A, B, C	A, B, C, D	A, B, D	C, D	C	B	A, B, C, D	D

Date class

1	2	3	4	5	6	7	8
A, B, C	A, B	A, B, C	B	B	B	A	A, B, C

Date - time class

1	2	3
A, B, C, D	A, B, C, D	D

If statement

1	2	3	4	5	6	7	8
A, B, D	B	B	C	B	B, D	A	A

Ternary statement

1	2	3	4	5	6
A, D	B	D	D	A, D	D

Switch statement

1	2	3	4	5	6
B	A, B, C, D	D	A	D	A, B, C, D

Salesforce Apex Question Bank

For loop

1	2	3	4	5
D	C	B	A	A

While loop

1	2	3	4	5
A	A	A	B	A

Do-while loop

1	2	3	4	5
D	A	D	D	B

Arrays

1	2	3	4	5
C	B, C	A	A	A, B, C

For-each loop

1	2	3	4	5
D	A	A	A	D

Lists

1	2	3	4	5	6	7
D	B	B	C	D	A	C

Sets

1	2	3	4	5
A	D	A, B, C	B	B

11	12	13	14	15	16	17	18

Maps

1	2	3	4	5
B	C	D	B	B

Made in the USA
Monee, IL
12 October 2022

15717297R00070